What gives an ocean motion?

LONDON, NEW YORK,
MELBOURNE, MUNICH, AND DELHI

DORLING KINDERSLEY
Project Editor Victoria Wiggins
Senior Designer Sheila Collins

Managing Editor Linda Esposito
Managing Art Editor Diane Peyton Jones

Category Publisher Laura Buller

Production Controller Sophie Argyris
Production Editor Rebekah Parsons-King

Jacket Editor Manisha Majithia
Jacket Designers Silke Spingies, Nim Kook

Publishing Director Jonathan Metcalf
Associate Publishing Director Liz Wheeler
Art Director Phil Ormerod

DORLING KINDERSLEY INDIA
Senior Art Editor Chhaya Sajwan
Art Editors Pankaj Bhatia, Suhita Dharamjit, Niyati Gosain, Shipra Jain, Nidhi Mehra, Namita, Payal Rosalind, Priyanka Singh, Shruti Soharia Singh, Dhirendra Singh, Amit Varma, Vidit Vashisht
Managing Art Editors Priyabrata Roy Chowdhury, Arunesh Talapatra
Senior Editor Monica Saigal
Editors Gaurav Joshi, Roma Malik, Suparna Sengupta
Managing Editor Pakshalika Jayaprakash
DTP Designers Rajesh Singh Adhikari, Neeraj Bhatia, Jaypal Singh Chauhan, Anita Yadav
DTP Manager Balwant Singh
Production Manager Pankaj Sharma
Picture Research Sakshi Saluja

First published in Great Britain in 2012
by Dorling Kindersley Limited
80 Strand, London WC2R 0RL

A Penguin Company

2 4 6 8 10 9 7 5 3 1
001—185369—02/07

A CIP catalogue record for this book is available from the British Library.

ISBN 978 1 4093 7647 7

Printed and bound by South China Printing Co. Ltd, China

See our complete catalogue at
www.dk.com

What gives an ocean motion?

Contributors: Kim Dennis-Bryan and John Woodward

Contents

Quiz number
Each quiz is numbered, so you can look up the relevant set of answers by quiz number.

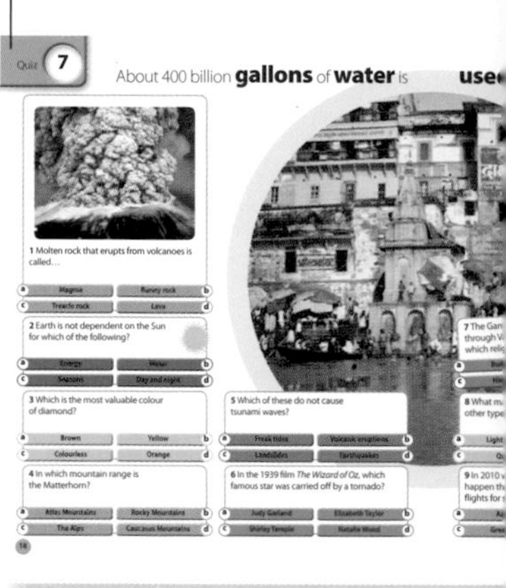

Reference

Earthquakes and tsunamis

Major earthquakes are among the most destructive natural disasters. They shake cities to the ground, and trigger tsunamis that result in catastrophic flooding. They are caused by the relentless movement of Earth's tectonic plates building up years of stress that is all released in a few seconds.

Catastrophe

Earthquakes strike without warning. The ground literally shakes, rocking buildings from side to side until they collapse. Cracks often open up in the ground, rupturing gas pipes and causing fires – and since the water pipes often break too there is no water to put the fires out.

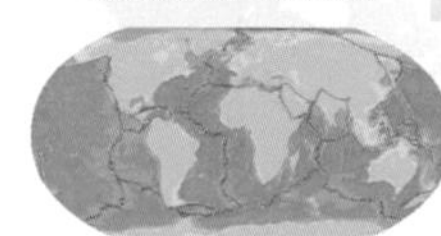

Grinding plates

Nearly all earthquakes occur in regions where the plates of Earth's crust are either pushing together or sliding past each other. These earthquake zones are shown in green on this map of the major plate boundaries.

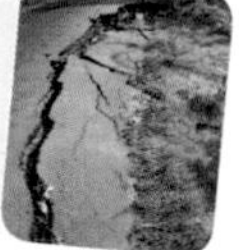

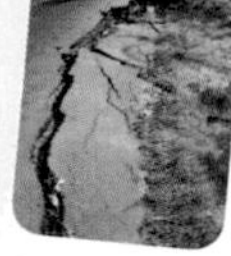

Creep and snap

Where the plates creep steadily past each other, the movement causes only minor damage, like this cracked road. But if they lock together, tension builds up until something snaps, triggering an earthquake.

How to use this book

Each quiz is given a difficulty rating – easy (green), medium (blue), or hard (red) – as well as a quiz number. The questions are also numbered, with multiple-choice answers. Each question is colour-coded, so you know which reference page to turn to if you want to find out more about a particular subject. The answers are laid out in a clear, easy-to-use section at the back of the book.

Picture questions
Every quiz has at least two picture questions, testing your visual memory.

Learning more
You'll find fun facts on every page.

Difficulty rating
Choose between easy, medium, and hard quizzes, depending on how bright you're feeling. The level of each quiz is clearly indicated.

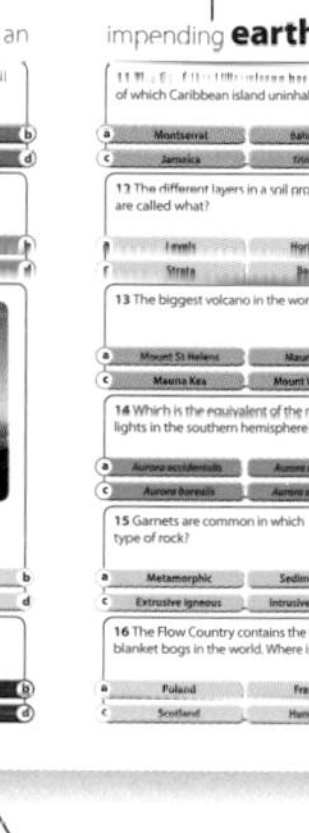

Reference colour
Match the colour of the question to the colour of the reference page tab, and find out more about the subjects that interest you.

Up to **300 million** people **live**

1 What is the depression in the peak of a volcano called?

- **a** Crater
- **b** Side
- **c** Cone
- **d** Chamber

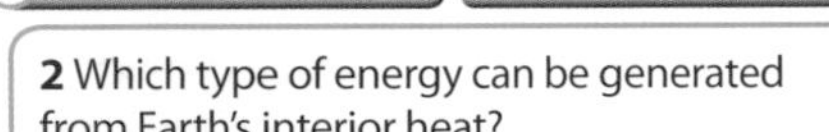

2 Which type of energy can be generated from Earth's interior heat?

- **a** Geothermal
- **b** Solar
- **c** Biogas
- **d** Nuclear

3 Who sang "Here Comes the Sun"?

- **a** The Rolling Stones
- **b** Elton John
- **c** The Beatles
- **d** Judy Garland

4 A scientist who studies rock is called a…

- **a** Meteorologist
- **b** Geologist
- **c** Rock hunter
- **d** Vulcanologist

5 Which term is used by geographers to describe a pointed mountain peak formed by glacial erosion?

- **a** Staggered summit
- **b** Pyramidal peak
- **c** Triangular peak
- **d** Shattered summit

6 Which ungulate once roamed the N American prairies in vast numbers?

- **a** White-tailed deer
- **b** Elk
- **c** American buffalo
- **d** Pronghorn

7 Which of these helped to carve out the rock of the Grand Canyon?

- **a** Gold mining
- **b** An ocean draining
- **c** A river
- **d** A meteorite

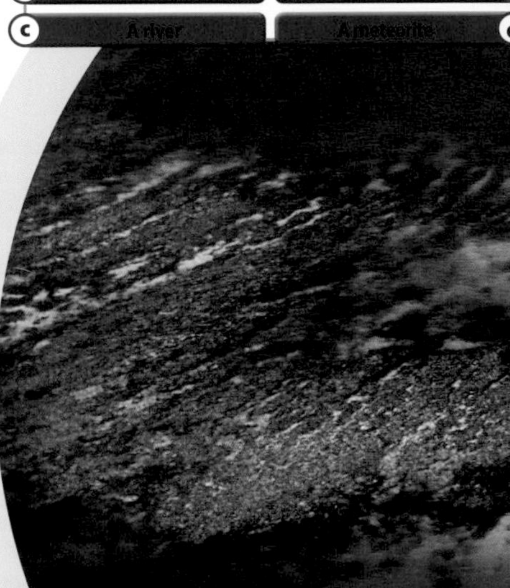

8 Vibrations triggered by earthquakes have led scientists to conclude that the planet's surface is like what?

- a An orange
- b A doughnut
- c An onion
- d An apple

9 What is thought to have created the craters on the Moon's surface?

- a Glacial action
- b Water erosion
- c Evaporation of oceans
- d Meteorite bombardment

10 The Great Barrier Reef is found in which sea?

- a Coral Sea
- b Sulu Sea
- c Timor Sea
- d Celebes Sea

11 Which month has an amethyst as its birthstone?

- a February
- b April
- c November
- d July

12 Which is the world's largest desert?

- a Kalahari
- b Sonoran
- c Atacama
- d Sahara

13 Which ocean current is associated with floods in America and droughts in Australia?

- a El Dorado
- b Gulf Stream
- c Pacific Stream
- d El Niño

14 Europe's tallest mountain is…

- a Mont Blanc
- b Mount Snowdon
- c The Matterhorn
- d Mount Elbrus

15 Which character in the *Ice Age* films creates tectonic plates while attempting to bury his prize acorn?

- a Manny
- b Scrat
- c Sid
- d Diego

Quiz 2

Shanghai, China, is the **most**

1 Which chemical element was not present when the first galaxies formed?

- a Neon
- b Lithium
- c Beryllium
- d Hydrogen

2 The French port of Le Havre is at the mouth of which river?

- a Seine
- b Rhine
- c Somme
- d Loire

3 In which time zone are the North and South poles located?

- a Paris Time
- b None
- c GMT
- d New York Time

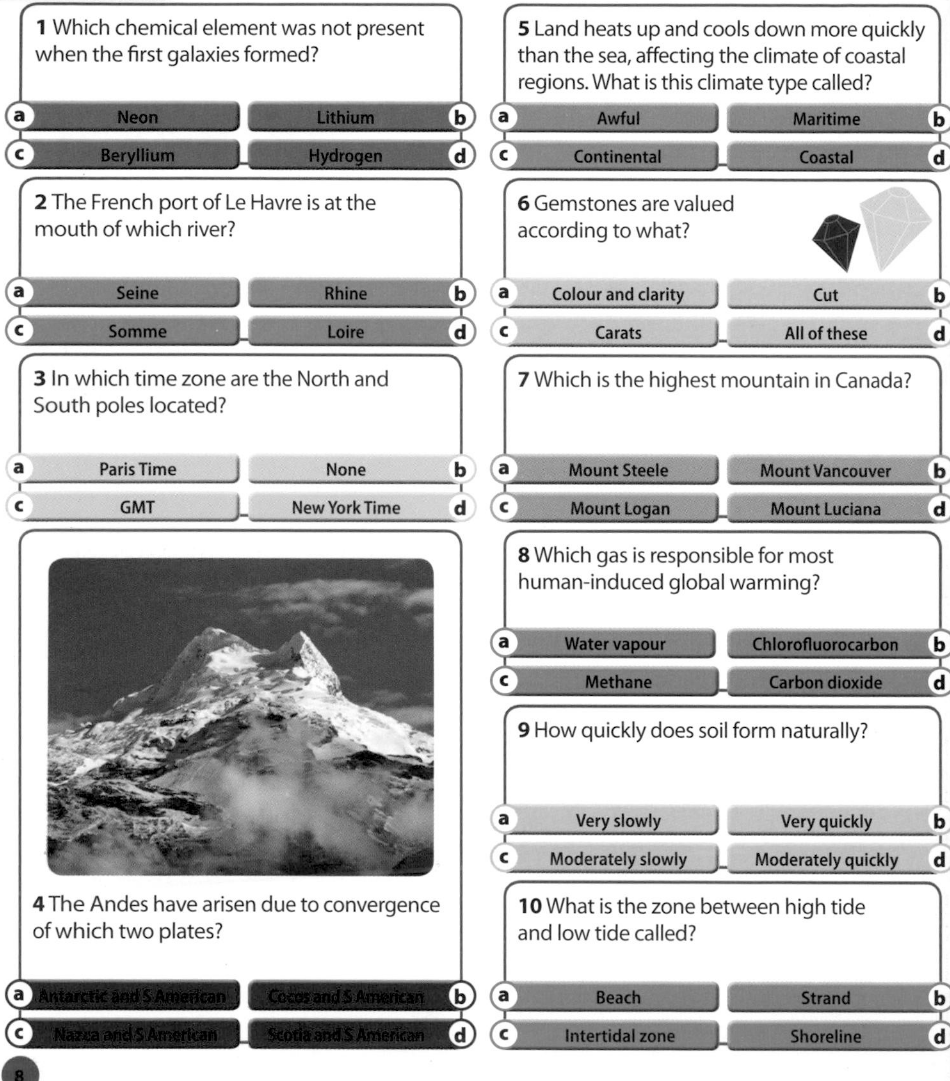

4 The Andes have arisen due to convergence of which two plates?

- a Antarctic and S American
- b Cocos and S American
- c Nazca and S American
- d Scotia and S American

5 Land heats up and cools down more quickly than the sea, affecting the climate of coastal regions. What is this climate type called?

- a Awful
- b Maritime
- c Continental
- d Coastal

6 Gemstones are valued according to what?

- a Colour and clarity
- b Cut
- c Carats
- d All of these

7 Which is the highest mountain in Canada?

- a Mount Steele
- b Mount Vancouver
- c Mount Logan
- d Mount Luciana

8 Which gas is responsible for most human-induced global warming?

- a Water vapour
- b Chlorofluorocarbon
- c Methane
- d Carbon dioxide

9 How quickly does soil form naturally?

- a Very slowly
- b Very quickly
- c Moderately slowly
- d Moderately quickly

10 What is the zone between high tide and low tide called?

- a Beach
- b Strand
- c Intertidal zone
- d Shoreline

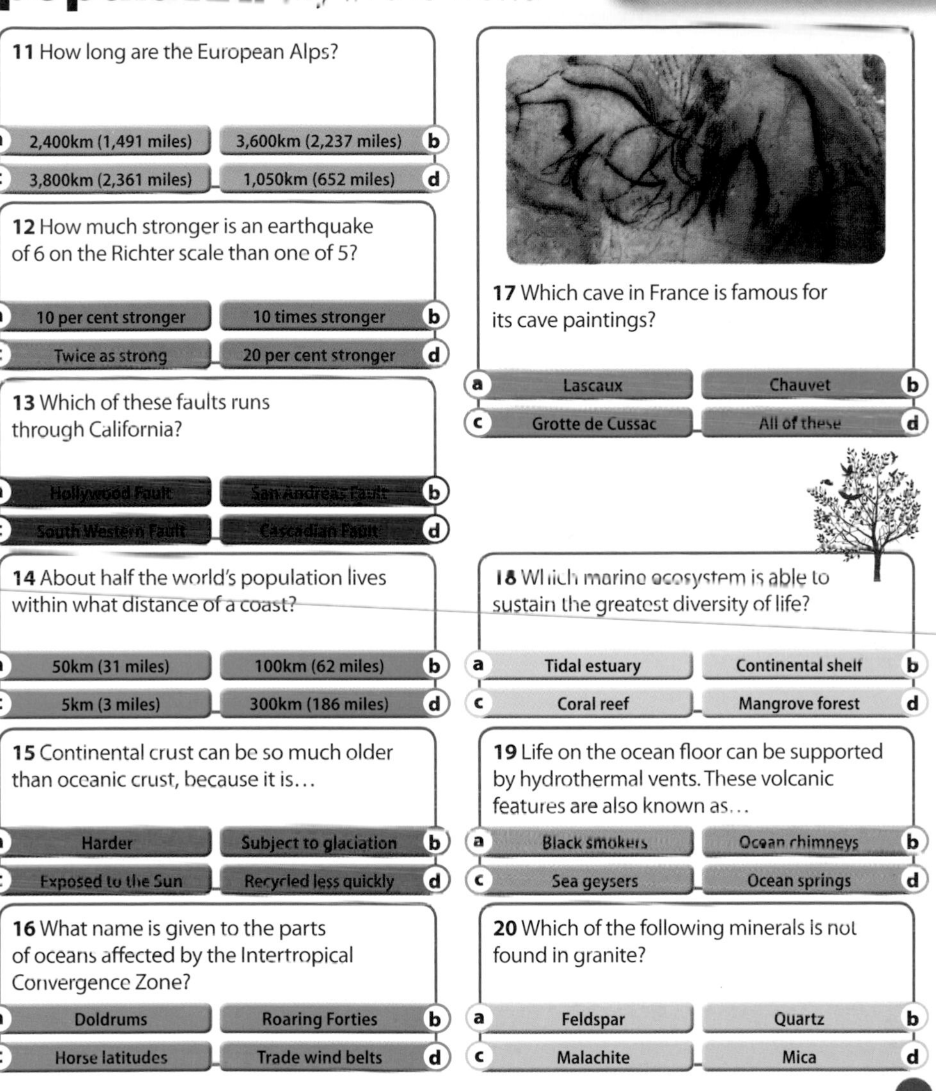

11 How long are the European Alps?

- a 2,400km (1,491 miles)
- b 3,600km (2,237 miles)
- c 3,800km (2,361 miles)
- d 1,050km (652 miles)

12 How much stronger is an earthquake of 6 on the Richter scale than one of 5?

- a 10 per cent stronger
- b 10 times stronger
- c Twice as strong
- d 20 per cent stronger

13 Which of these faults runs through California?

- a Hollywood Fault
- b San Andreas Fault
- c South Western Fault
- d Cascadian Fault

14 About half the world's population lives within what distance of a coast?

- a 50km (31 miles)
- b 100km (62 miles)
- c 5km (3 miles)
- d 300km (186 miles)

15 Continental crust can be so much older than oceanic crust, because it is…

- a Harder
- b Subject to glaciation
- c Exposed to the Sun
- d Recycled less quickly

16 What name is given to the parts of oceans affected by the Intertropical Convergence Zone?

- a Doldrums
- b Roaring Forties
- c Horse latitudes
- d Trade wind belts

17 Which cave in France is famous for its cave paintings?

- a Lascaux
- b Chauvet
- c Grotte de Cussac
- d All of these

18 Which marine ecosystem is able to sustain the greatest diversity of life?

- a Tidal estuary
- b Continental shelf
- c Coral reef
- d Mangrove forest

19 Life on the ocean floor can be supported by hydrothermal vents. These volcanic features are also known as…

- a Black smokers
- b Ocean chimneys
- c Sea geysers
- d Ocean springs

20 Which of the following minerals is not found in granite?

- a Feldspar
- b Quartz
- c Malachite
- d Mica

Hillary and **Norgay** were the

1 Besides a meteor strike, the extinction of the dinosaurs is also attributed to volcanic activity in...

a India
b China
c Mongolia
d Russia

2 Approximately how long after the Universe formed did stable helium and hydrogen atoms appear?

a 300,000 years
b 1 million years
c 750,000 years
d Immediately after

3 Which African lake has shrunk to one-fifth of its original size over the past 50 years?

a Nyasa
b Volta
c Chad
d Malawi

4 On the Richter scale, what is the highest rating ever recorded for an earthquake?

a 3
b 9.5
c 8
d 6.4

5 Which river connects Lake Superior with Lake Michigan?

a River Detroit
b River Ottawa
c River St Marys
d River St Clair

6 Which of the following are not fold mountains?

a Himalayas
b Andes
c Harz
d Alps

7 Which is the fine-grained equivalent of granite?

a Syenite
b Rhyolite
c Pegmatite
d Gabbro

8 Who devised the system of naming clouds, which is still used today?

a Theodore Fujita
b Vilhelm Bjerknes
c Milutin Milankovic
d Luke Howard

9 What is the scientific term for the formation of mountain ranges where continental plates collide and crumple?

a Cordillera
b Orogeny
c Orology
d Geology

10 Which metamorphic rock is often used on the roofs of houses?

a Gneiss
b Skarn
c Slate
d Schist

11 When the Sun's rays fall on snow and ice, how much of it is reflected?

- a 90 per cent
- b 70 per cent
- c 50 per cent
- d 30 per cent

12 Where is the coastline that gives a Dalmatian coast its name?

- a Bulgaria
- b Croatia
- c Turkey
- d Germany

13 At what annual rate is the Mid-Atlantic Ridge diverging?

- a 0.5cm (0.19in)
- b 4cm (1.5in)
- c 2cm (0.78in)
- d 5cm (1.9in)

14 Which seismic waves are used to calculate the Richter magnitude of an earthquake?

- a Rayleigh waves
- b Love waves
- c P waves
- d S waves

15 Which type of feature is the Corryvreckan, which lies off the coast of Jura in the west of Scotland?

- a Whirlpool
- b Reef with shipwrecks
- c Underwater canyon
- d Unexploded bomb

16 Who is responsible for the theory of continental drift?

- a John Tuzo Wilson
- b Abraham Werner
- c Andrija Mohorovicic
- d Alfred Wegener

17 Which area of wetland covers much of southern Florida?

- a Wakodahatchee Wetland
- b Everglades
- c Axe Lake Swamp
- d Mississippi River Delta

18 In which process do waves hit the beach at an angle and move material along the coast?

- a Refraction
- b Deflection
- c Downshore drift
- d Longshore drift

19 Which of the following is not on the Moon?

- a Sea of Tranquility
- b Sea of Serenity
- c Sea of Islands
- d Sea of Asov

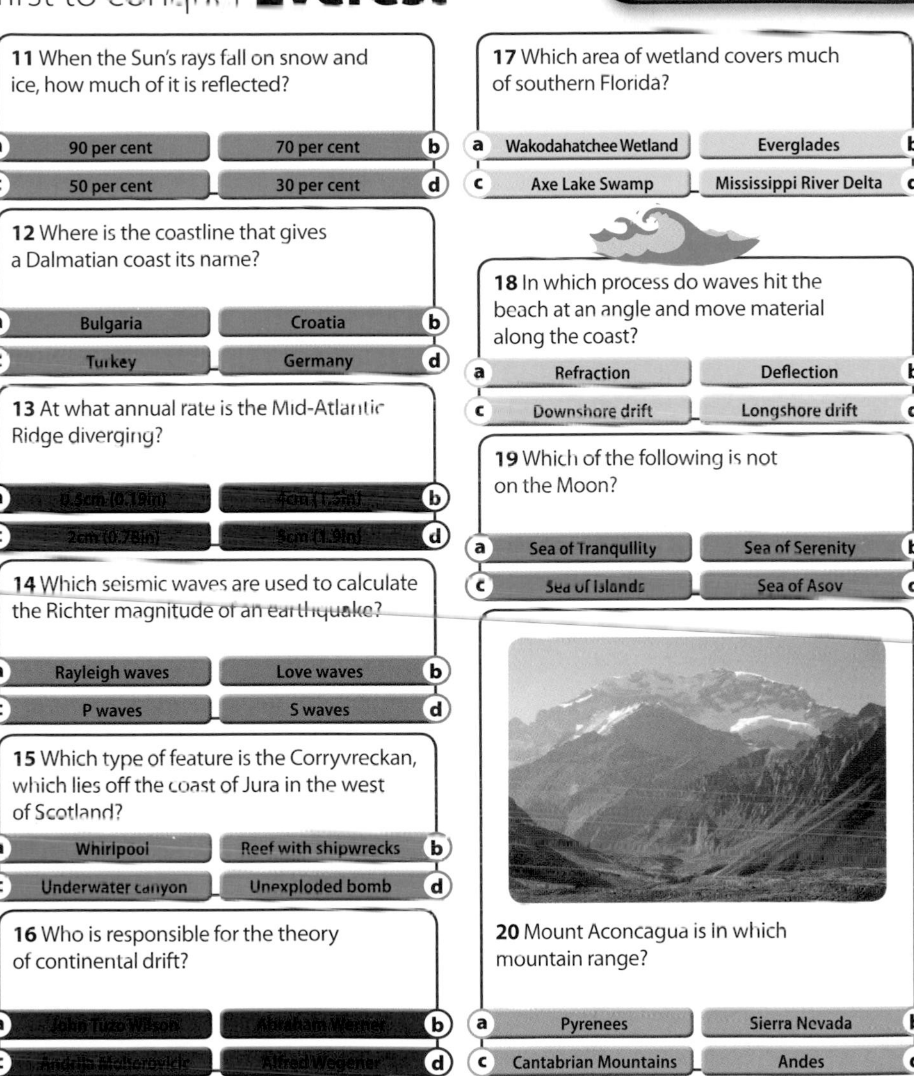

20 Mount Aconcagua is in which mountain range?

- a Pyrenees
- b Sierra Nevada
- c Cantabrian Mountains
- d Andes

Quiz 4

Complex **life** on Earth **evolved**

1 What is the main cause of tides?

- a Earthquakes
- b Wind
- c Gravity of the Moon
- d Gravity of the planets

2 Which adaptation helps protect cacti from being eaten by animals?

- a Spines
- b Bad taste
- c Bad smell
- d Ugly appearance

3 What speed can the winds reach in a large tornado?

- a 800kph (497mph)
- b 400kph (249mph)
- c 80kph (50mph)
- d 500kph (311mph)

4 What is Earth's core mostly made of?

- a Ice
- b Iron
- c Silicon
- d Aluminium

5 What happens when two tectonic plates are moving apart?

- a Convergence
- b Transformation
- c Subduction
- d Divergence

6 What colour is sulphur?

- a White
- b Light blue
- c Yellow
- d Green

600 million years ago

7 Which book of the Bible tells the story of Noah and the flood?

a Exodus
b Leviticus
c Deuteronomy
d Genesis

8 Which of these mountains is not a volcano?

a Mount Fuji
b Mount Cook
c Mount Stromboli
d Mount Ararat

9 Who proved that lightning was electricity?

a Benjamin Franklin
b Isaac Newton
c Michael Faraday
d Thomas Edison

10 What is the rarest cause of a tsunam

a Meteorite impact
Earthquake
c Underwater landslide
d Volcanic eruption

11 Which of these deserts is not in Africa?

a Sahara
b Kalahari
c Namib
d Gobi

12 Which of these in Earth's history is a snowball event?

a Period of glaciation
b Meteorite shower
c Higher wind speeds
d Lower sunspot activity

13 Which river flows through Varanasi?

a Sutlej
b Ganges
c Indus
d Brahmaputra

14 Precious stones form by crystallization of minerals deep underground. Which of these is not a precious stone?

a Ruby
b Topaz
c Diamond
d Coral

15 How high is Mount Everest?

a 6,750m (22,146ft)
b 5,800m (19,029ft)
c 8,848m (29,029ft)
d 10,150m (33,301ft)

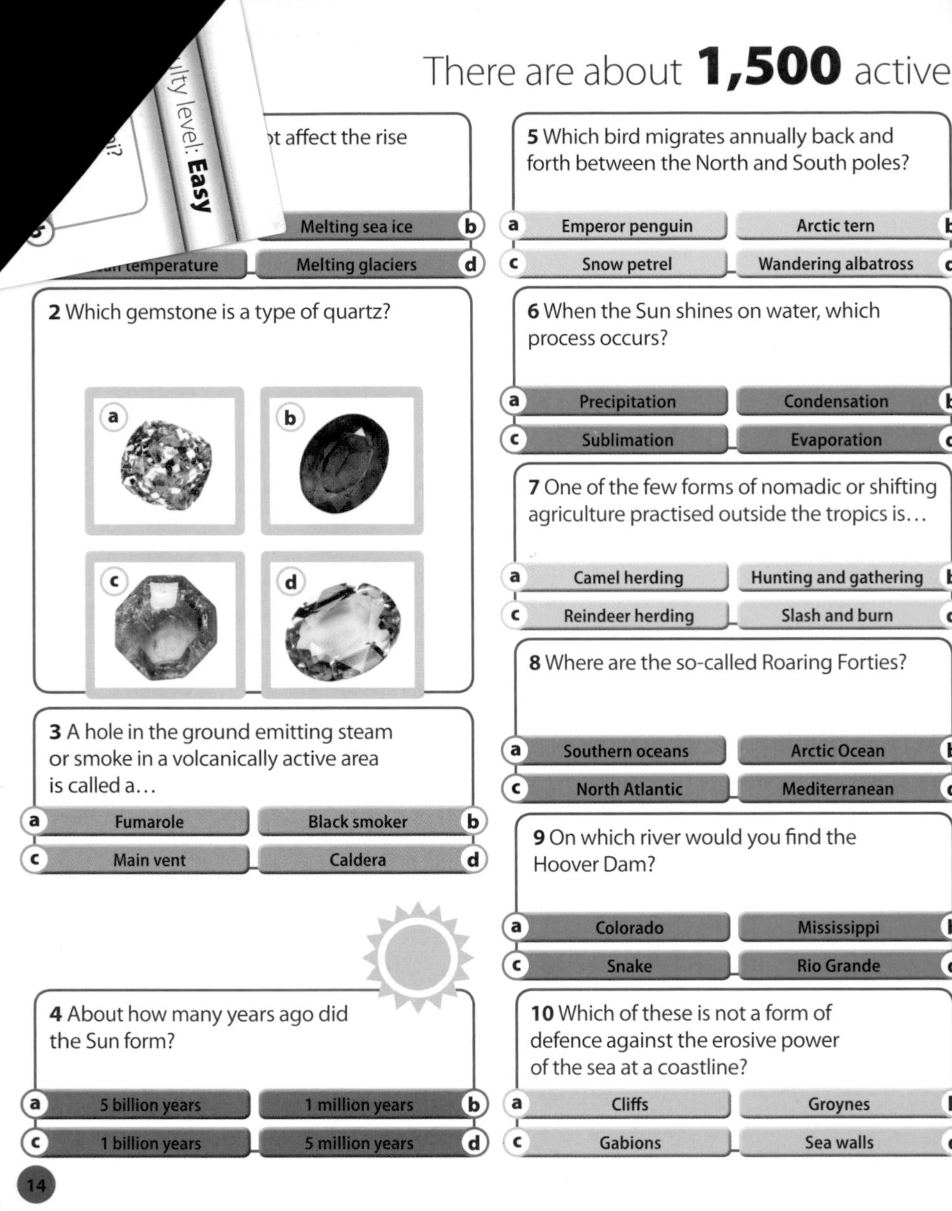

There are about **1,500** active

…lty level: **Easy**

…i?

1 …t affect the rise

a	…	Melting sea ice	b
c	…temperature	Melting glaciers	d

2 Which gemstone is a type of quartz?

a, b, c, d

3 A hole in the ground emitting steam or smoke in a volcanically active area is called a…

a	Fumarole	Black smoker	b
c	Main vent	Caldera	d

4 About how many years ago did the Sun form?

a	5 billion years	1 million years	b
c	1 billion years	5 million years	d

5 Which bird migrates annually back and forth between the North and South poles?

a	Emperor penguin	Arctic tern	b
c	Snow petrel	Wandering albatross	d

6 When the Sun shines on water, which process occurs?

a	Precipitation	Condensation	b
c	Sublimation	Evaporation	d

7 One of the few forms of nomadic or shifting agriculture practised outside the tropics is…

a	Camel herding	Hunting and gathering	b
c	Reindeer herding	Slash and burn	d

8 Where are the so-called Roaring Forties?

a	Southern oceans	Arctic Ocean	b
c	North Atlantic	Mediterranean	d

9 On which river would you find the Hoover Dam?

a	Colorado	Mississippi	b
c	Snake	Rio Grande	d

10 Which of these is not a form of defence against the erosive power of the sea at a coastline?

a	Cliffs	Groynes	b
c	Gabions	Sea walls	d

11 Approximately what percentage of an iceberg is visible above water?

a 27 per cent
b 9 per cent
c 13 per cent
d 4 per cent

12 Which is the most common extrusive igneous rock?

a Trachyte
b Phonolite
c Basalt
d Andesite

13 Tectonic plates increase in size due to what?

a Subduction
b Accretion
c Sea-floor spreading
d Divergence

14 What is the haze that forms in polluted air in strong sunshine called?

a Fog
b Mist
c Rain
d Smog

15 Which is the main source of oil pollution at sea?

a Natural oil seepage
b Shipping
c Industrial waste
d Offshore oil production

16 In which direction did Laurasia drift?

a West
b North
c South
d East

17 The different layers of the atmosphere are separated by height and…

a Gas composition
b Water vapour
c Human influence
d Temperature range

18 Approximately what percentage of the world's surface is covered by mountains?

a 2 per cent
b 1 per cent
c 10 per cent
d 7 per cent

19 Which is the point on Earth's surface that lies directly over the site of the ruptured fault in an earthquake?

a Wave point
b Shock centre
c Epicentre
d Zone zero

20 Where was the Hooker Emerald mined?

a Peru
b Brazil
c Ecuador
d Colombia

The **Pacific Ocean** covers about

1 How many types of minerals are there?

- a) More than 2,000
- b) About 10,000
- c) More than 4,000
- d) About 500

2 In 2007 how much of the Arctic's normal summer sea-ice cover melted?

- a) 60 per cent
- b) 40 per cent
- c) 50 per cent
- d) All of it

3 This is Bryce Canyon, Utah. What are these strange-looking structures called?

- a) Hoodoos
- b) Limestone stacks
- c) Karst
- d) Totem poles

4 How many chemical elements were there when galaxies started to form?

- a) 6
- b) 2
- c) 8
- d) 4

5 Which is the longest cave system in the world?

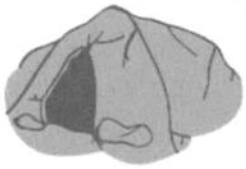

- a) Cango Caves
- b) Gunung Mulu
- c) Mammoth Caves
- d) Carlsbad Caves

6 Tectonic plates are in constant motion. How far might a plate move in one year?

- a) 1m (3ft)
- b) 1cm (0.4in)
- c) 15cm (6in)
- d) 30cm (12in)

7 In 1963 which Icelandic volcano erupted and created a new island?

- a) Grimsvotn
- b) Surtsey
- c) Eyjafjallajökull
- d) Hekla

8 Which US city was damaged by an earthquake and subsequent fire in April 1906?

- a) New York
- b) Boston
- c) San Francisco
- d) Los Angeles

9 Which name is given to tropical storms that affect the coast of Japan?

- a) Typhoon
- b) Cyclone
- c) Hurricane
- d) Tsunami

10 Which is the largest freshwater lake in the world?

- a) Great Bear
- b) Lake Superior
- c) Lake Victoria
- d) Lake Baikal

11 In which wetland region does much of the White Nile's water evaporate?

a Rufiji-Mafia-Kilwa
b Sudd
c Qattara Depression
d Malagarasi

12 Which is the largest lake in Italy?

a Maggiore
b Como
c Lugano
d Garda

13 When were the first instruments for measuring earthquakes developed?

a 1940s
b 1880s
c 1900s
d 1920s

14 What is the science of Earth's physical structure called?

a Geophysics
b Geography
c Palaeontology
d Geology

15 Which of the following are not dome mountains?

a Black Hills
b Adirondacks
c Navajo Mountain
d Sierra Nevada

16 What, according to the saying, "makes the world go round"?

a Love
b Gravity
c Music
d The Sun

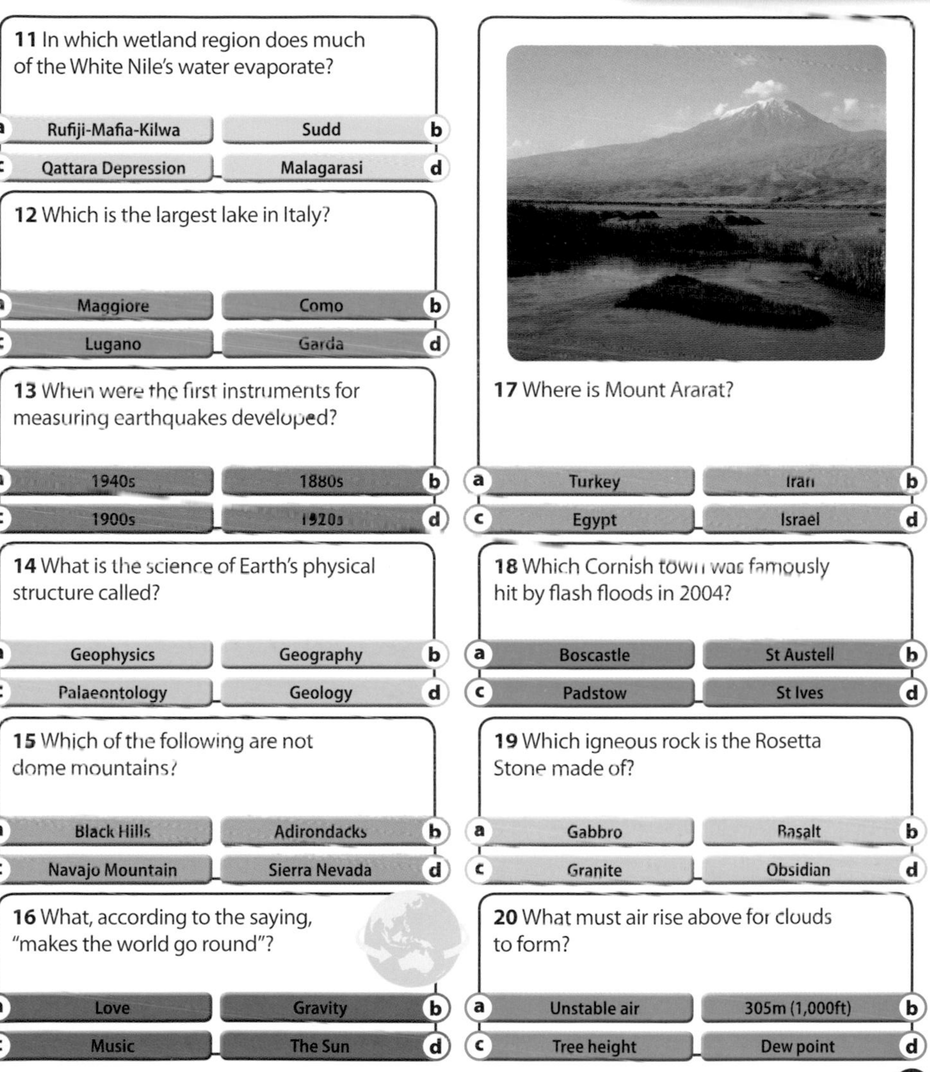

17 Where is Mount Ararat?

a Turkey
b Iran
c Egypt
d Israel

18 Which Cornish town was famously hit by flash floods in 2004?

a Boscastle
b St Austell
c Padstow
d St Ives

19 Which igneous rock is the Rosetta Stone made of?

a Gabbro
b Basalt
c Granite
d Obsidian

20 What must air rise above for clouds to form?

a Unstable air
b 305m (1,000ft)
c Tree height
d Dew point

Quiz 7

About 400 billion **gallons** of **water** is

1 Molten rock that erupts from volcanoes is called…

2 Earth is not dependent on the Sun for which of the following?

3 Which is the most valuable colour of diamond?

4 In which mountain range is the Matterhorn?

5 Which of these do not cause tsunami waves?

a Freak tides
b Volcanic eruptions
c Landslides
d Earthquakes

6 In the 1939 film *The Wizard of Oz*, which famous star was carried off by a tornado?

a Judy Garland
b Elizabeth Taylor
c Shirley Temple
d Natalie Wood

7 The Ganges – pictured here flowing through Varanasi – is sacred to which religion?

- **a** Buddhism
- **b** Jainism
- **c** Hinduism
- **d** Sikhism

8 What may sedimentary rocks have that other types of rock do not?

- **a** Light colours
- **b** Fossils
- **c** Quartz
- **d** Large crystals

9 In 2010 where did the volcanic eruption happen that grounded all transatlantic flights for several days?

- **a** Azores
- **b** Iceland
- **c** Greenland
- **d** Canada

10 Which of these human activities are detrimental to forests?

- **a** Pollution
- **b** Slash and burn
- **c** Fragmentation
- **d** All of these

11 The walls of the Grand Canyon are made up of layers of rock. Where are the youngest rocks?

- **a** At the bottom
- **b** In the middle
- **c** Not visible
- **d** At the top

12 How hot is Earth's inner core?

- **a** 25°C (77°F)
- **b** –50°C (–58°F)
- **c** 7,000°C (12,632°F)
- **d** 700°C (1,292°F)

13 Which of these is not caused by movement of Earth's plates?

- **a** Sedimentation
- **b** Volcanoes
- **c** Earthquakes
- **d** Mountain formation

14 During which time of the day are animals most active in the desert?

- **a** Noon
- **b** Night
- **c** Evening
- **d** Morning

15 What percentage of Earth's surface is covered by water?

- **a** 13 per cent
- **b** 52 per cent
- **c** 99 per cent
- **d** 71 per cent

Quiz 8

The oldest existing **rocks** are more than

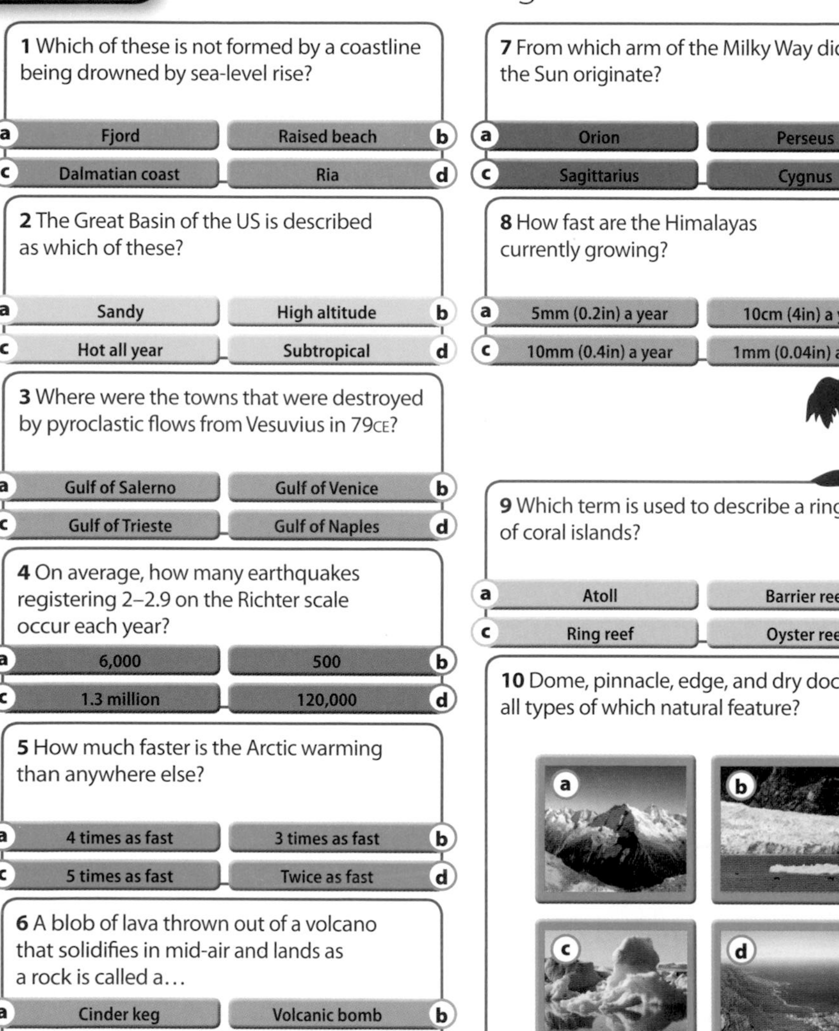

1 Which of these is not formed by a coastline being drowned by sea-level rise?

- a Fjord
- b Raised beach
- c Dalmatian coast
- d Ria

2 The Great Basin of the US is described as which of these?

- a Sandy
- b High altitude
- c Hot all year
- d Subtropical

3 Where were the towns that were destroyed by pyroclastic flows from Vesuvius in 79CE?

- a Gulf of Salerno
- b Gulf of Venice
- c Gulf of Trieste
- d Gulf of Naples

4 On average, how many earthquakes registering 2–2.9 on the Richter scale occur each year?

- a 6,000
- b 500
- c 1.3 million
- d 120,000

5 How much faster is the Arctic warming than anywhere else?

- a 4 times as fast
- b 3 times as fast
- c 5 times as fast
- d Twice as fast

6 A blob of lava thrown out of a volcano that solidifies in mid-air and lands as a rock is called a…

- a Cinder keg
- b Volcanic bomb
- c Pyroclastic flow
- d Magma ball

7 From which arm of the Milky Way did the Sun originate?

- a Orion
- b Perseus
- c Sagittarius
- d Cygnus

8 How fast are the Himalayas currently growing?

- a 5mm (0.2in) a year
- b 10cm (4in) a year
- c 10mm (0.4in) a year
- d 1mm (0.04in) a year

9 Which term is used to describe a ring of coral islands?

- a Atoll
- b Barrier reef
- c Ring reef
- d Oyster reef

10 Dome, pinnacle, edge, and dry dock are all types of which natural feature?

a b c d

4.25 billion years **old**

Difficulty level: **Medium**

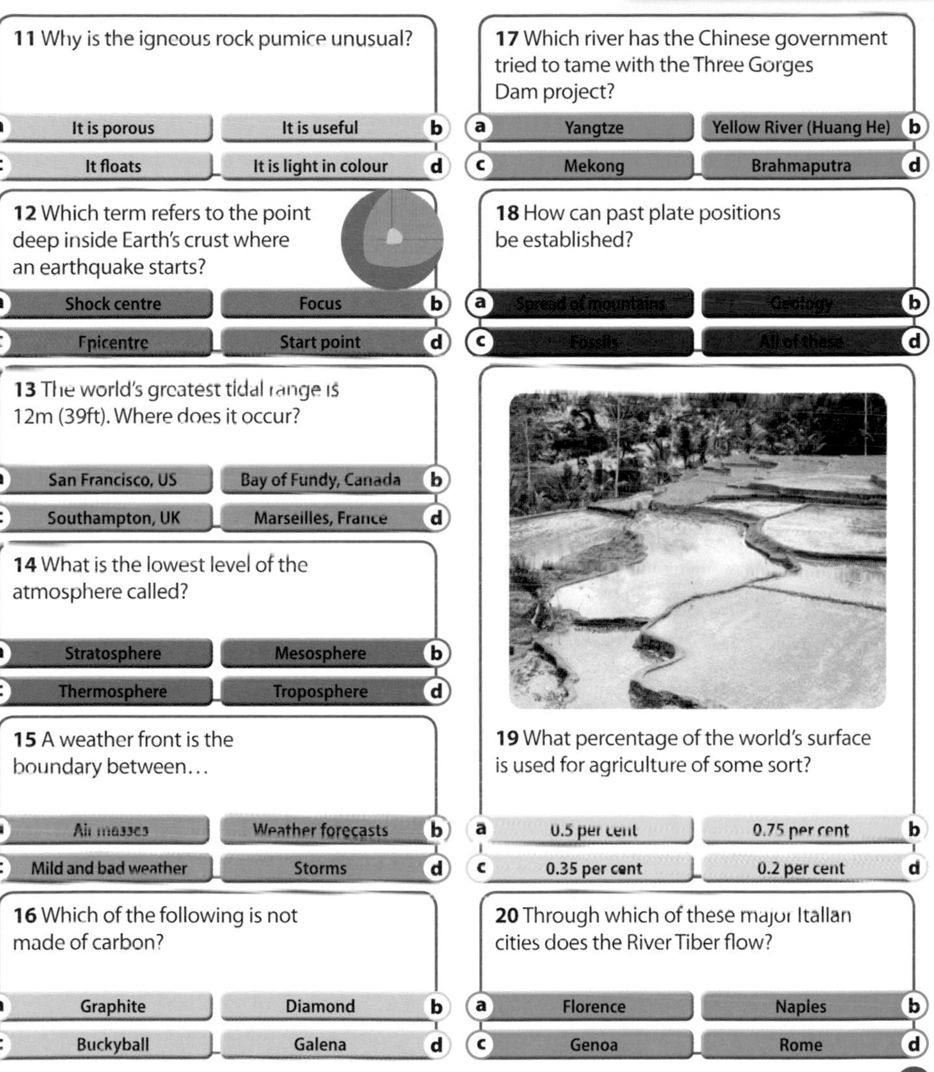

11 Why is the igneous rock pumice unusual?

a It is porous
b It is useful
c It floats
d It is light in colour

12 Which term refers to the point deep inside Earth's crust where an earthquake starts?

a Shock centre
b Focus
c Epicentre
d Start point

13 The world's greatest tidal range is 12m (39ft). Where does it occur?

a San Francisco, US
b Bay of Fundy, Canada
c Southampton, UK
d Marseilles, France

14 What is the lowest level of the atmosphere called?

a Stratosphere
b Mesosphere
c Thermosphere
d Troposphere

15 A weather front is the boundary between…

a Air masses
b Weather forecasts
c Mild and bad weather
d Storms

16 Which of the following is not made of carbon?

a Graphite
b Diamond
c Buckyball
d Galena

17 Which river has the Chinese government tried to tame with the Three Gorges Dam project?

a Yangtze
b Yellow River (Huang He)
c Mekong
d Brahmaputra

18 How can past plate positions be established?

a Spread of mountains
b Geology
c Fossils
d All of these

19 What percentage of the world's surface is used for agriculture of some sort?

a 0.5 per cent
b 0.75 per cent
c 0.35 per cent
d 0.2 per cent

20 Through which of these major Italian cities does the River Tiber flow?

a Florence
b Naples
c Genoa
d Rome

Antarctica comes from a Greek word

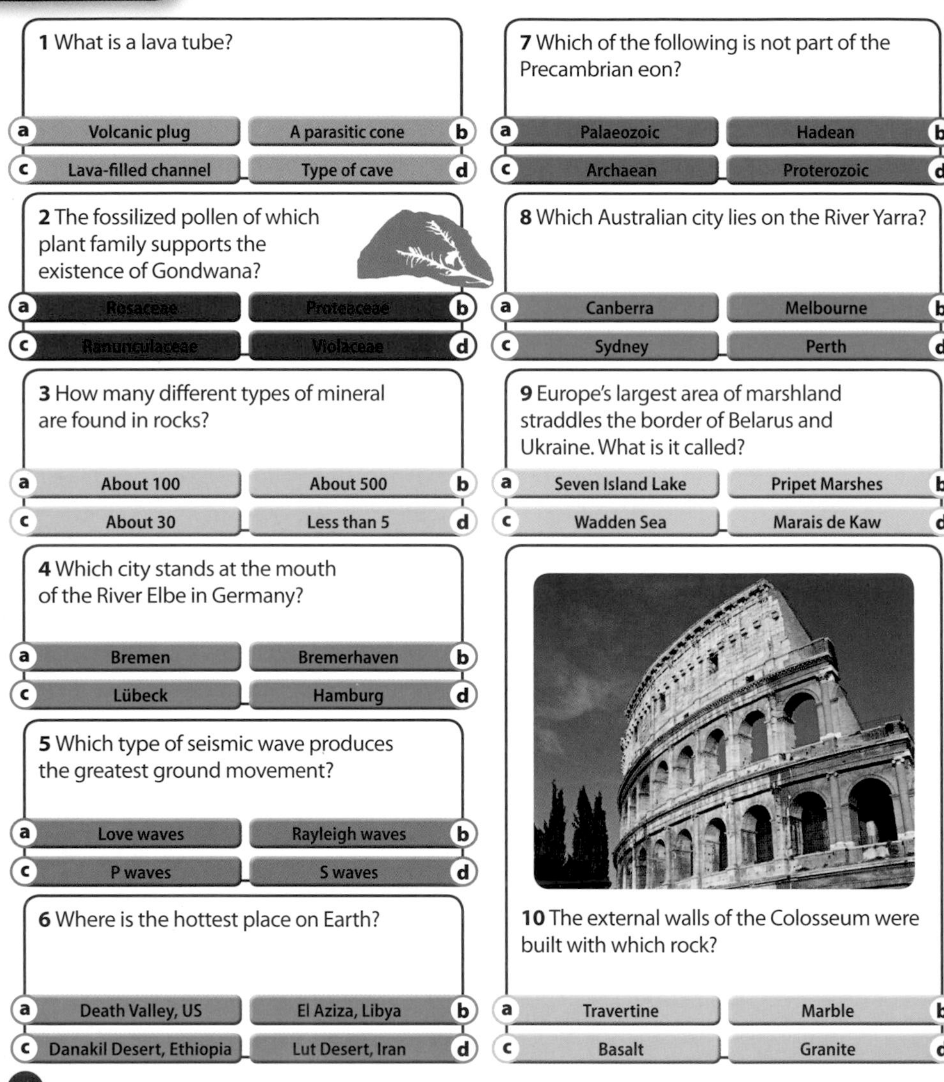

1 What is a lava tube?

- a Volcanic plug
- b A parasitic cone
- c Lava-filled channel
- d Type of cave

2 The fossilized pollen of which plant family supports the existence of Gondwana?

- a Rosaceae
- b Proteaceae
- c Ranunculaceae
- d Violaceae

3 How many different types of mineral are found in rocks?

- a About 100
- b About 500
- c About 30
- d Less than 5

4 Which city stands at the mouth of the River Elbe in Germany?

- a Bremen
- b Bremerhaven
- c Lübeck
- d Hamburg

5 Which type of seismic wave produces the greatest ground movement?

- a Love waves
- b Rayleigh waves
- c P waves
- d S waves

6 Where is the hottest place on Earth?

- a Death Valley, US
- b El Aziza, Libya
- c Danakil Desert, Ethiopia
- d Lut Desert, Iran

7 Which of the following is not part of the Precambrian eon?

- a Palaeozoic
- b Hadean
- c Archaean
- d Proterozoic

8 Which Australian city lies on the River Yarra?

- a Canberra
- b Melbourne
- c Sydney
- d Perth

9 Europe's largest area of marshland straddles the border of Belarus and Ukraine. What is it called?

- a Seven Island Lake
- b Pripet Marshes
- c Wadden Sea
- d Marais de Kaw

10 The external walls of the Colosseum were built with which rock?

- a Travertine
- b Marble
- c Basalt
- d Granite

11 What job do "pisteurs" have in the Swiss Alps?

a Setting off avalanches
b Preparing ski equipment
c Repairing ski lifts
d Teaching people to ski

12 Which of these did not give his name to a scale for measuring earthquakes?

a Richter
b Gutenberg
c Wegener
d Mercalli

13 Who discovered the Rosetta Stone?

a Wilfred Thesiger
b Napoleon's troops
c Alexander the Great
d Lord Carnarvon

14 What hit King's Heath, Birmingham, in July 2005 and Kensal Rise, London, in December 2006?

a Tornado
b Flash flood
c Giant hailstones
d Thick fog

15 Oceanic crust always subducts beneath continental crust. Why is this?

a Water weighs it down
b It is softer
c It is denser
d It is thinner

16 If you are going white-water rafting and your route is given a rating of Class 1, it is…

a Very gentle
b Quite fast
c Fast and dangerous
d Very dangerous

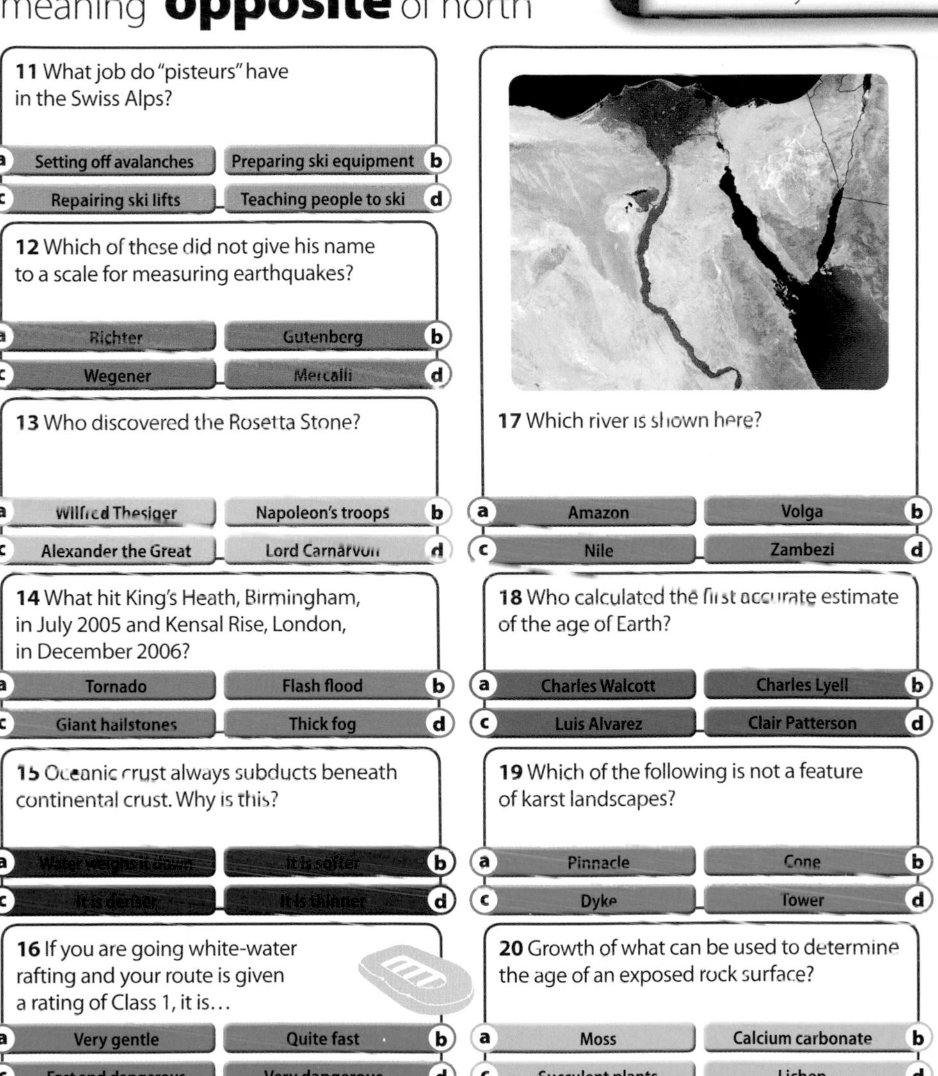

17 Which river is shown here?

a Amazon
b Volga
c Nile
d Zambezi

18 Who calculated the first accurate estimate of the age of Earth?

a Charles Walcott
b Charles Lyell
c Luis Alvarez
d Clair Patterson

19 Which of the following is not a feature of karst landscapes?

a Pinnacle
b Cone
c Dyke
d Tower

20 Growth of what can be used to determine the age of an exposed rock surface?

a Moss
b Calcium carbonate
c Succulent plants
d Lichen

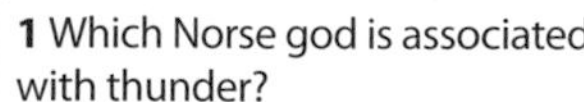

About **75 per cent** of Earth's surface

1 Which Norse god is associated with thunder?

a Thor
b Loki
c Odin
d Ve

2 How long does it take for Earth to orbit the Sun?

a 365 days
b 31 days
c 365¼ days
d 24 hours

3 Which mountain is pictured here?

a Mauna Loa
b Mount Sinai
c Uluru
d Mount Kilimanjaro

4 Which of these deserts is not in N America?

a Sonoran
b Patagonian
c Chihuahuan
d Mojave

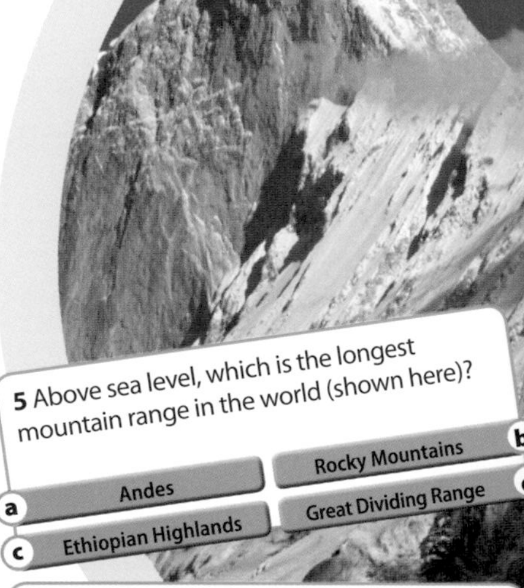

5 Above sea level, which is the longest mountain range in the world (shown here)?

a Andes
b Rocky Mountains
c Ethiopian Highlands
d Great Dividing Range

6 Rocks that fall to Earth from space are called what?

a Comets
b Asteroids
c Storms
d Meteorites

7 Which term do meteorologists use to describe the noise made by a lightning bolt?

a Sky clap
b Lightning bang
c Thunder
d Storm boom

8 The start of a river is called its…

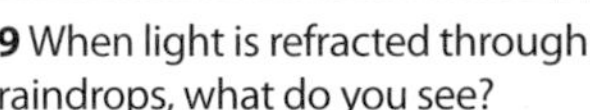
9 When light is refracted through raindrops, what do you see?

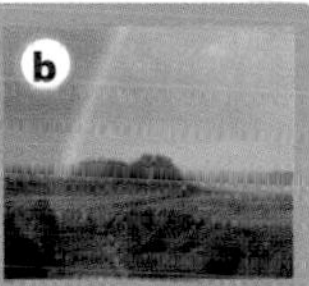

10 Which major layer comes between Earth's core and crust?

11 What are tsunamis also known as?

12 In which US state is the Grand Canyon?

13 Who was the first man to reach the South Pole?

14 Which of the following often occurs near faults or cracks in Earth's crust?

15 Where would you go to see the Koh-i-Noor diamond?

a Tower of London
b Bank of England
c British Museum
d Chatsworth House

Mauna Kea is taller than **Everest**,

1 In which mountains can the Kea parrot be found?

a) Southern Alps
b) Great Dividing Range
c) Crocker Mountains
d) Trus Madi Range

2 What are the most coarse-grained sedimentary rocks called?

a) Limestones
b) Conglomerates
c) Aggregates
d) Sandstones

3 What name is given to the expanse of ocean over which the wind blows to generate waves?

a) Fetch
b) Carry
c) Longshore
d) Length

4 Which volcanic hazard consists of deadly superheated gas and rock particles?

a) Lava flow
b) Volcanic bomb
c) Lahar
d) Pyroclastic flow

5 Which is the largest river system?

a) Amazon
b) Nile
c) Mississippi
d) Congo

6 Following an earthquake in 1906, much of the city of San Francisco in the US was destroyed by what?

a) Tsunamis
b) Fire
c) Flooding
d) Landslides

7 A landmass made up of more than one continental core or craton is called what?

a) Plate
b) Supercontinent
c) Continent
d) Shield

8 Which is the largest lake in the Alps?

a) Constance
b) Neuchâtel
c) Lucerne
d) Geneva

9 Coral reefs are made of which type of rock?

a) Sandstone
b) Shale
c) Clay
d) Limestone

10 High-pressure systems are associated with which type of weather?

a) Humid and cloudy
b) Very windy
c) Wet and cloudy
d) Dry with clear skies

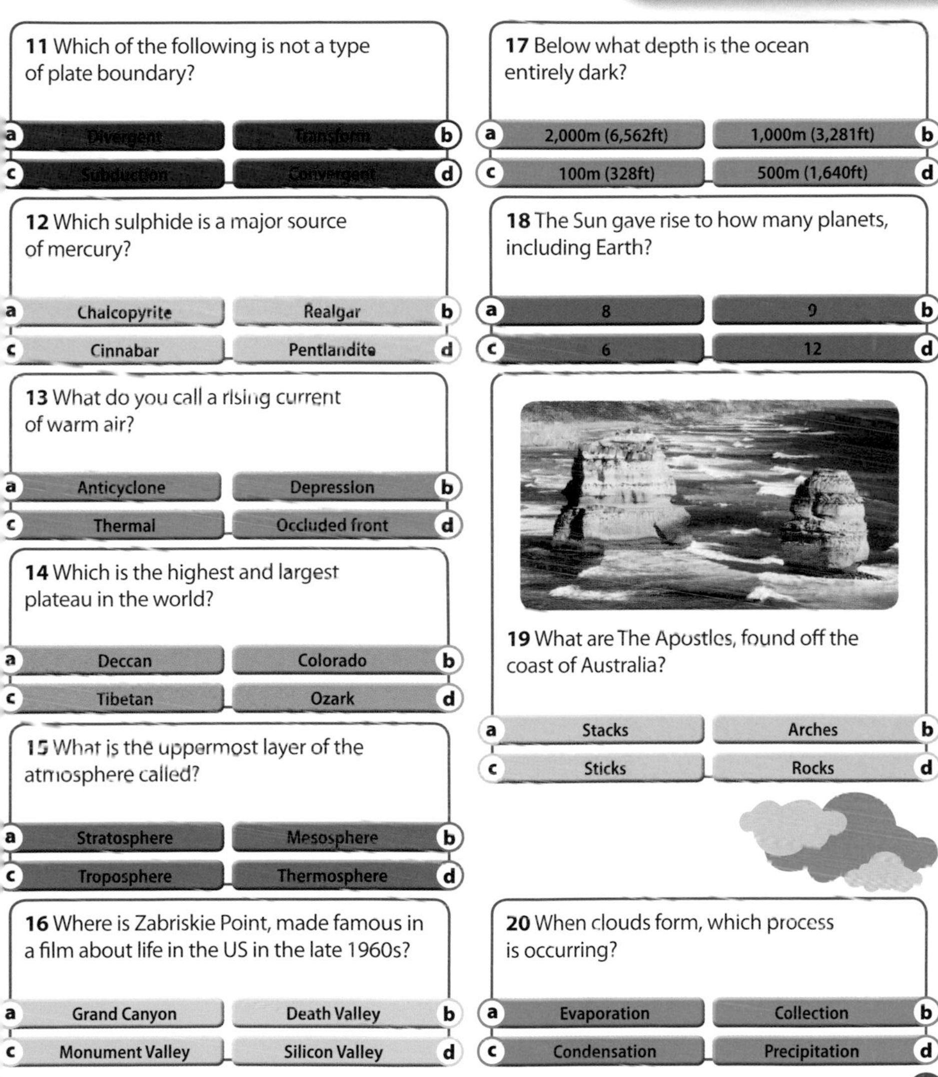

11 Which of the following is not a type of plate boundary?

a Divergent | b Transform
c Subduction | d Convergent

12 Which sulphide is a major source of mercury?

a Chalcopyrite | b Realgar
c Cinnabar | d Pentlandite

13 What do you call a rising current of warm air?

a Anticyclone | b Depression
c Thermal | d Occluded front

14 Which is the highest and largest plateau in the world?

a Deccan | b Colorado
c Tibetan | d Ozark

15 What is the uppermost layer of the atmosphere called?

a Stratosphere | b Mesosphere
c Troposphere | d Thermosphere

16 Where is Zabriskie Point, made famous in a film about life in the US in the late 1960s?

a Grand Canyon | b Death Valley
c Monument Valley | d Silicon Valley

17 Below what depth is the ocean entirely dark?

a 2,000m (6,562ft) | b 1,000m (3,281ft)
c 100m (328ft) | d 500m (1,640ft)

18 The Sun gave rise to how many planets, including Earth?

a 8 | b 9
c 6 | d 12

19 What are The Apostles, found off the coast of Australia?

a Stacks | b Arches
c Sticks | d Rocks

20 When clouds form, which process is occurring?

a Evaporation | b Collection
c Condensation | d Precipitation

Quiz 12

Krakatoa's 1883 **eruption** released energy

1 If an earthquake happens in your school, what is the official advice for you?

a) Quickly run outside
b) Press the fire alarm
c) Stand still until it stops
d) Duck, cover, and hold on

2 Crater Lake in the US has formed inside an extinct volcano. Which of these records does it hold?

a) Deepest in US
b) Largest in US
c) Most acidic in US
d) Saltiest in US

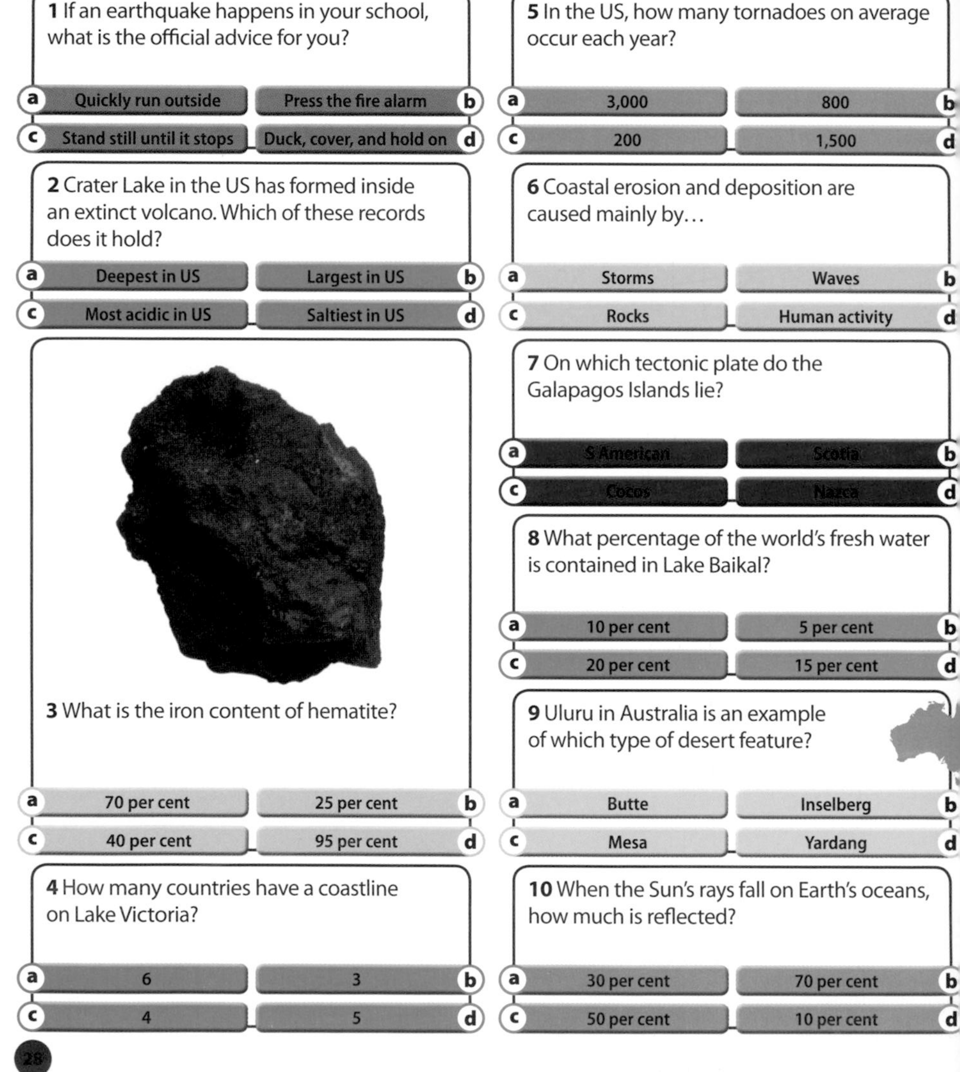

3 What is the iron content of hematite?

a) 70 per cent
b) 25 per cent
c) 40 per cent
d) 95 per cent

4 How many countries have a coastline on Lake Victoria?

a) 6
b) 3
c) 4
d) 5

5 In the US, how many tornadoes on average occur each year?

a) 3,000
b) 800
c) 200
d) 1,500

6 Coastal erosion and deposition are caused mainly by…

a) Storms
b) Waves
c) Rocks
d) Human activity

7 On which tectonic plate do the Galapagos Islands lie?

a) S American
b) Scotia
c) Cocos
d) Nazca

8 What percentage of the world's fresh water is contained in Lake Baikal?

a) 10 per cent
b) 5 per cent
c) 20 per cent
d) 15 per cent

9 Uluru in Australia is an example of which type of desert feature?

a) Butte
b) Inselberg
c) Mesa
d) Yardang

10 When the Sun's rays fall on Earth's oceans, how much is reflected?

a) 30 per cent
b) 70 per cent
c) 50 per cent
d) 10 per cent

11 Which is the deepest-known cave?

a Skocjanske Jame
b Gouffre Mirolda
c Krubera
d Optimisticheskaya

12 Who wrote the 1912 novel *The Lost World*, which describes an ill-fated expedition to the Amazon Basin?

a Sir Arthur Conan Doyle
b F Scott Fitzgerald
c J K Rowling
d Ernest Hemingway

13 Mammatus clouds form in the base of which other type of cloud?

a Cumulonimbus
b Altostratus
c Cirrocumulus
d Stratus

14 These Italian mountains are almost entirely made up of which rock-forming mineral?

a Hematite
b Calcite
c Dolomite
d Magnetite

15 Which of these volcanoes lies on the Italian island of Sicily?

a Lipari
b Etna
c Vesuvius
d Stromboli

16 What is tuff?

a Swarm of volcanic bombs
b Compressed pumice
c Compacted volcanic ash
d Lithified quartz

17 In which year did a massive tsunami kill 2,200 people in Papua New Guinea?

a 1960
b 1930
c 1998
d 2005

18 How fast can basaltic lava flow?

a Up to 100kph (62mph)
b Up to 25kph (16mph)
c Up to 50kph (31mph)
d Up to 75kph (47mph)

19 The River Neva flows into which gulf of the Baltic Sea?

a Bothnia
b Danzig
c Riga
d Finland

20 Minerals are classified into groups. How many groups are there?

a 6
b 18
c 27
d 10

About **20 per cent** of the world's

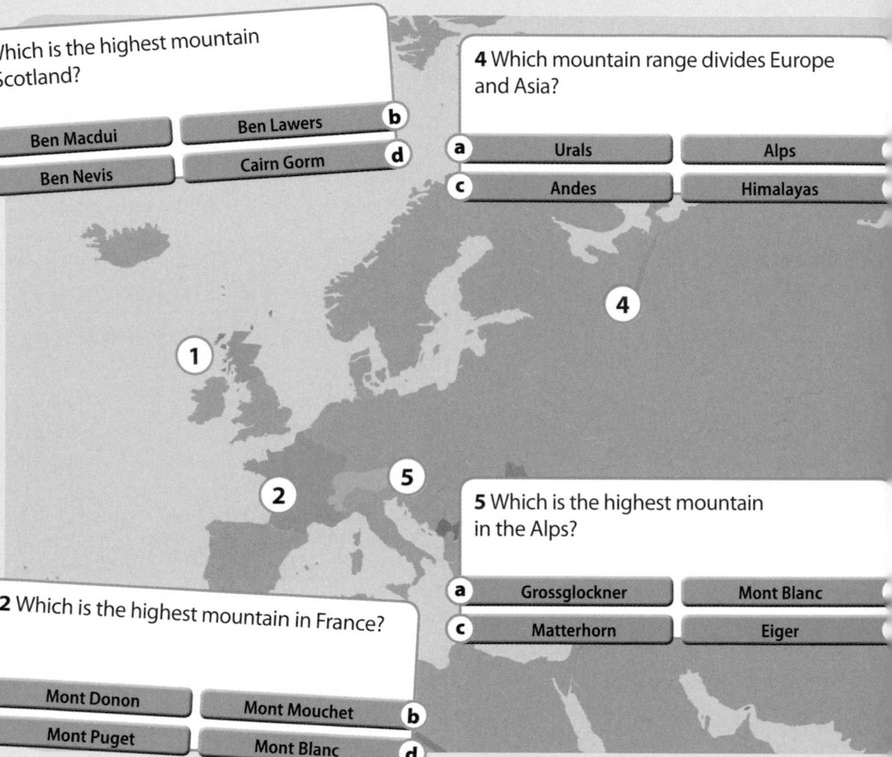

1 Which is the highest mountain in Scotland?

a Ben Macdui
b Ben Lawers
c Ben Nevis
d Cairn Gorm

4 Which mountain range divides Europe and Asia?

a Urals
b Alps
c Andes
d Himalayas

5 Which is the highest mountain in the Alps?

a Grossglockner
b Mont Blanc
c Matterhorn
d Eiger

2 Which is the highest mountain in France?

a Mont Donon
b Mont Mouchet
c Mont Puget
d Mont Blanc

3 Which term is used to describe the calm centre of a tropical storm?

a Ear
b Supercell
c Eye
d Core

6 How long does it take for Earth to rotate once about its axis?

a 1 week
b 1 month
c 365 days
d 24 hours

fresh water is in Lake Baikal

Difficulty level: **Easy**

7 Which of the following is not a type of opal?

a Fire | b Black | c White | d Wind

8 What happens when a tsunami wave enters shallower water?

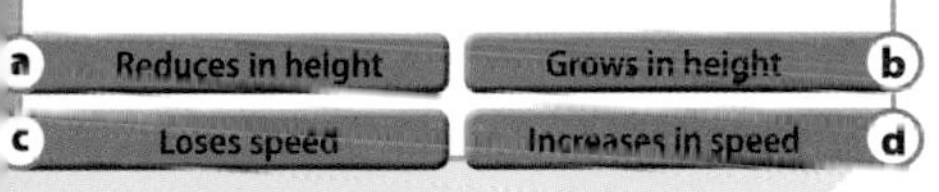

a Reduces in height | b Grows in height | c Loses speed | d Increases in speed

9 Hunters in the S American rainforest use poison-tipped arrows. Where does the poison come from?

a Fungi | b Fish | c Frogs | d Plants

10 Earth's surface is split into plates that are always…

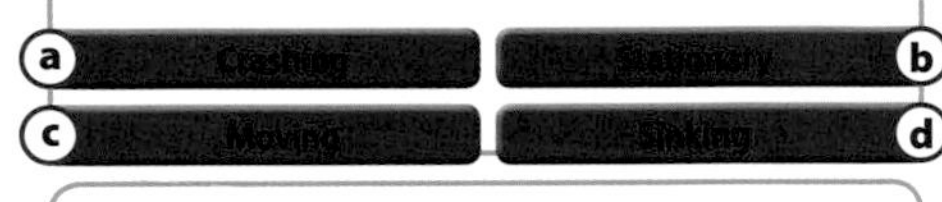

a Crashing | b Stationary | c Moving | d Sinking

11 What colour is Earth's atmosphere when seen from space?

a Blue | b Orange | c White | d Colourless

12 What are the people that track and study tornadoes close-up called?

a Storm roadies | b Storm chasers | c Storm crews | d Storm runners

13 Which kind of desert people move home frequently in search of fresh grazing pastures for their animals?

a Settlers | b Movers | c Groupies | d Nomads

14 What are small rivers flowing into a larger main river called?

a Tributaries | b Distributaries | c Rivulets | d Junctions

15 The word geology is based on the Greek for what?

a Earth-study | b Ground-study | c Rocks | d Earth-logic

Quiz **14**

There are more than **1 million** minor

1 When do winds generally blow from sea to land?

- a Always
- b Afternoon
- c Night
- d Dawn

2 In which desert is the Empty Quarter?

- a Takla Makan
- b Gobi
- c Arabian
- d Sahara

3 Which of these geological terms refers to an area of unusually high volcanic activity?

- a Fracture zone
- b Hotspot
- c Volcanic spot
- d Break point

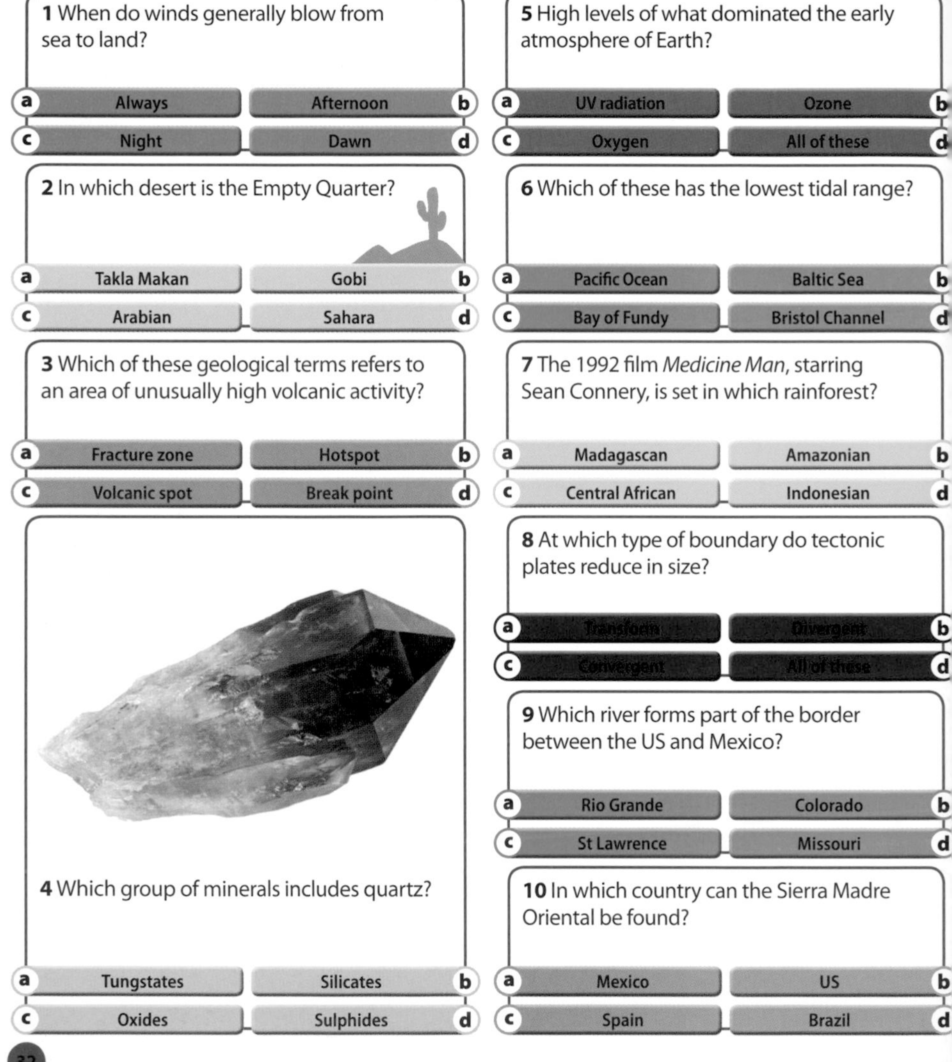

4 Which group of minerals includes quartz?

- a Tungstates
- b Silicates
- c Oxides
- d Sulphides

5 High levels of what dominated the early atmosphere of Earth?

- a UV radiation
- b Ozone
- c Oxygen
- d All of these

6 Which of these has the lowest tidal range?

- a Pacific Ocean
- b Baltic Sea
- c Bay of Fundy
- d Bristol Channel

7 The 1992 film *Medicine Man*, starring Sean Connery, is set in which rainforest?

- a Madagascan
- b Amazonian
- c Central African
- d Indonesian

8 At which type of boundary do tectonic plates reduce in size?

- a Transform
- b Divergent
- c Convergent
- d All of these

9 Which river forms part of the border between the US and Mexico?

- a Rio Grande
- b Colorado
- c St Lawrence
- d Missouri

10 In which country can the Sierra Madre Oriental be found?

- a Mexico
- b US
- c Spain
- d Brazil

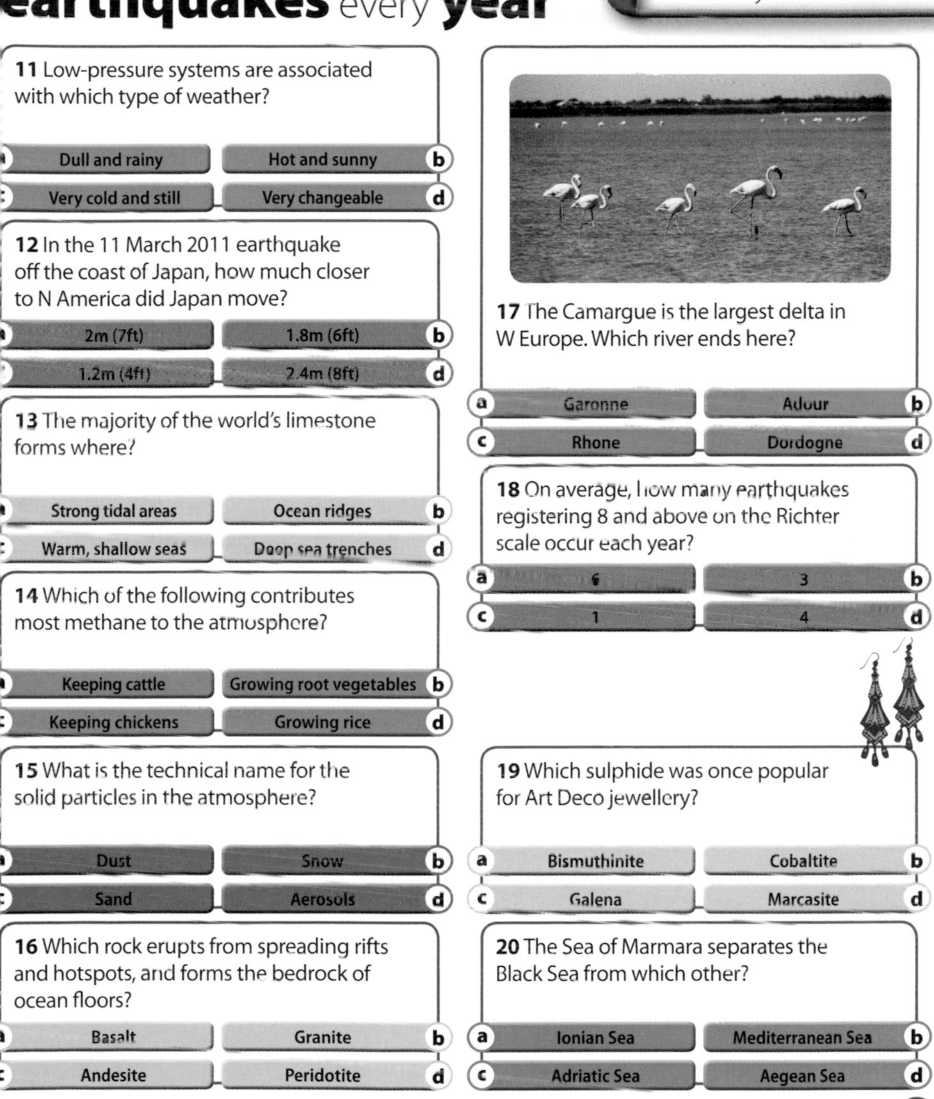

11 Low-pressure systems are associated with which type of weather?

a Dull and rainy | b Hot and sunny
c Very cold and still | d Very changeable

12 In the 11 March 2011 earthquake off the coast of Japan, how much closer to N America did Japan move?

a 2m (7ft) | b 1.8m (6ft)
c 1.2m (4ft) | d 2.4m (8ft)

13 The majority of the world's limestone forms where?

a Strong tidal areas | b Ocean ridges
c Warm, shallow seas | d Deep sea trenches

14 Which of the following contributes most methane to the atmosphere?

a Keeping cattle | b Growing root vegetables
c Keeping chickens | d Growing rice

15 What is the technical name for the solid particles in the atmosphere?

a Dust | b Snow
c Sand | d Aerosols

16 Which rock erupts from spreading rifts and hotspots, and forms the bedrock of ocean floors?

a Basalt | b Granite
c Andesite | d Peridotite

17 The Camargue is the largest delta in W Europe. Which river ends here?

a Garonne | b Adour
c Rhone | d Dordogne

18 On average, how many earthquakes registering 8 and above on the Richter scale occur each year?

a 6 | b 3
c 1 | d 4

19 Which sulphide was once popular for Art Deco jewellery?

a Bismuthinite | b Cobaltite
c Galena | d Marcasite

20 The Sea of Marmara separates the Black Sea from which other?

a Ionian Sea | b Mediterranean Sea
c Adriatic Sea | d Aegean Sea

15

An average **cloud weighs**

1 Which type of glacier dominates Alaska's Malaspina Glacier?

- a Outlet
- b Cirque
- c Piedmont
- d Valley

2 When was the Nakaya Snowflake Classification Chart first used?

- a 1951
- b 1969
- c 1980
- d 1935

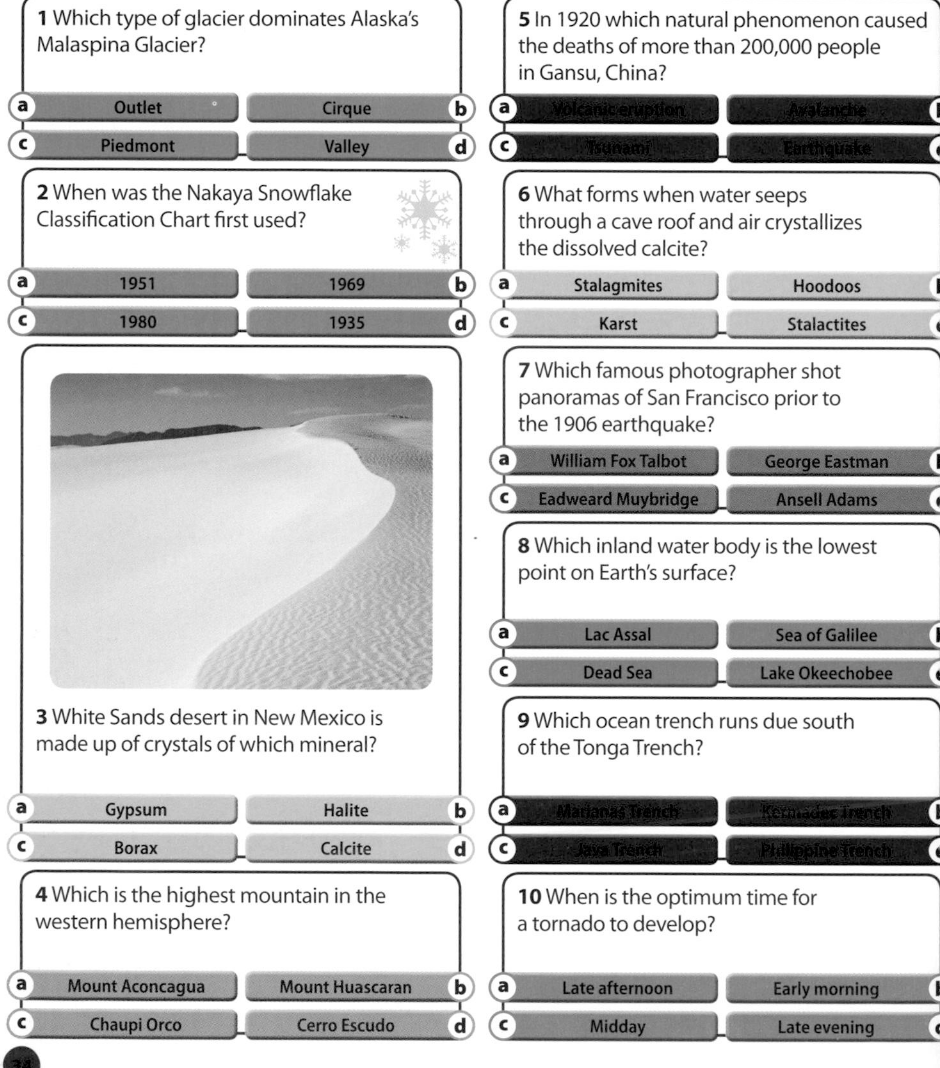

3 White Sands desert in New Mexico is made up of crystals of which mineral?

- a Gypsum
- b Halite
- c Borax
- d Calcite

4 Which is the highest mountain in the western hemisphere?

- a Mount Aconcagua
- b Mount Huascaran
- c Chaupi Orco
- d Cerro Escudo

5 In 1920 which natural phenomenon caused the deaths of more than 200,000 people in Gansu, China?

- a Volcanic eruption
- b Avalanche
- c Tsunami
- d Earthquake

6 What forms when water seeps through a cave roof and air crystallizes the dissolved calcite?

- a Stalagmites
- b Hoodoos
- c Karst
- d Stalactites

7 Which famous photographer shot panoramas of San Francisco prior to the 1906 earthquake?

- a William Fox Talbot
- b George Eastman
- c Eadweard Muybridge
- d Ansell Adams

8 Which inland water body is the lowest point on Earth's surface?

- a Lac Assal
- b Sea of Galilee
- c Dead Sea
- d Lake Okeechobee

9 Which ocean trench runs due south of the Tonga Trench?

- a Marianas Trench
- b Kermadec Trench
- c Java Trench
- d Philippine Trench

10 When is the optimum time for a tornado to develop?

- a Late afternoon
- b Early morning
- c Midday
- d Late evening

as much as a **jumbo jet**

Difficulty level: **Hard**

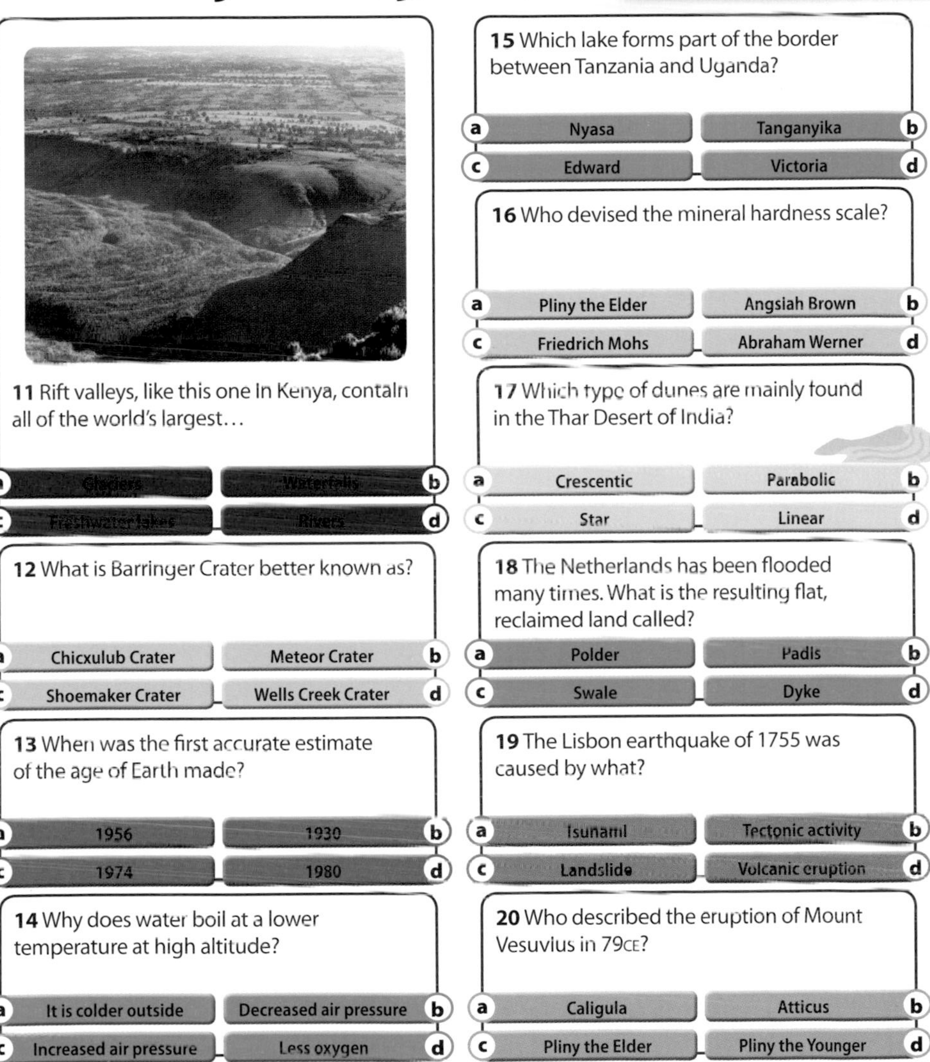

11 Rift valleys, like this one in Kenya, contain all of the world's largest…

a) Glaciers
b) Waterfalls
c) Freshwater lakes
d) Rivers

12 What is Barringer Crater better known as?

a) Chicxulub Crater
b) Meteor Crater
c) Shoemaker Crater
d) Wells Creek Crater

13 When was the first accurate estimate of the age of Earth made?

a) 1956
b) 1930
c) 1974
d) 1980

14 Why does water boil at a lower temperature at high altitude?

a) It is colder outside
b) Decreased air pressure
c) Increased air pressure
d) Less oxygen

15 Which lake forms part of the border between Tanzania and Uganda?

a) Nyasa
b) Tanganyika
c) Edward
d) Victoria

16 Who devised the mineral hardness scale?

a) Pliny the Elder
b) Angsiah Brown
c) Friedrich Mohs
d) Abraham Werner

17 Which type of dunes are mainly found in the Thar Desert of India?

a) Crescentic
b) Parabolic
c) Star
d) Linear

18 The Netherlands has been flooded many times. What is the resulting flat, reclaimed land called?

a) Polder
b) Padis
c) Swale
d) Dyke

19 The Lisbon earthquake of 1755 was caused by what?

a) Tsunami
b) Tectonic activity
c) Landslide
d) Volcanic eruption

20 Who described the eruption of Mount Vesuvius in 79CE?

a) Caligula
b) Atticus
c) Pliny the Elder
d) Pliny the Younger

Quiz **16**

About **one** in **every 10**

1 When is the Sun overhead at the Tropic of Cancer?

a June
b December
c September
d March

2 Which weather hazard is created by the build-up of static in storm clouds?

a Lightning
b Hailstones
c Torrential rain
d Gusty winds

3 Which metamorphic rock was used in the construction of the Taj Mahal?

a Hornfels
b Migmatite
c Marble
d Gneiss

4 Which mountain range forms the border between Chile and Argentina?

a Andes
b Pyrenees
c Caucasus
d Urals

5 Earthquakes that precede the main quake are referred to as what?

a Early tremors
b Preshocks
c Anteshocks
d Foreshocks

6 What is a crack in a glacier called?

a Crevasse
b Ravine
c Gully
d Fissure

7 What do scientists think happened 4.5 billion years ago?

a Pyramids were built
b Earth formed
c Dinosaurs appeared
d First human appeared

8 A desert is defined as a place with less than how much rain each year?

a 500mm (20in)
b 100mm (4in)
c 50mm (2in)
d 250mm (10in)

9 Which is the world's greatest river in terms of both volume of water and the size of its basin?

a Congo
b Amazon
c Nile
d Mississippi

10 Where would you find hot climates with year-round rain?

a In temperate latitudes
b At high altitude
c In polar regions
d In the tropics

people lives on an **island**

Difficulty level: **Easy**

11 Which volcano, shown here, is Japan's highest peak?

- a Mount Kilimanjaro
- b Mount Fuji
- c Mount Horoshiri-Dake
- d K2

12 In a river, which size of sediment is carried furthest out to sea?

- a Medium
- b Fine
- c Coarse
- d Mixture

13 The Equator divides Earth into two halves. What are they called?

- a Domes
- b Sectors
- c Zones
- d Hemispheres

14 Which is the largest tectonic plate?

- a Indian
- b African
- c Pacific
- d Eurasian

15 Which of the following is not a greenhouse gas?

- a Water vapour
- b Methane
- c Oxygen
- d Carbon dioxide

Quiz 17

99 per cent of Antarctica is

1 Mountains are attacked by the icy climate that causes rocks to shatter and crumble. What is this process called?

- a Biological weathering
- b Chemical weathering
- c Onion-skin weathering
- d Freeze-thaw weathering

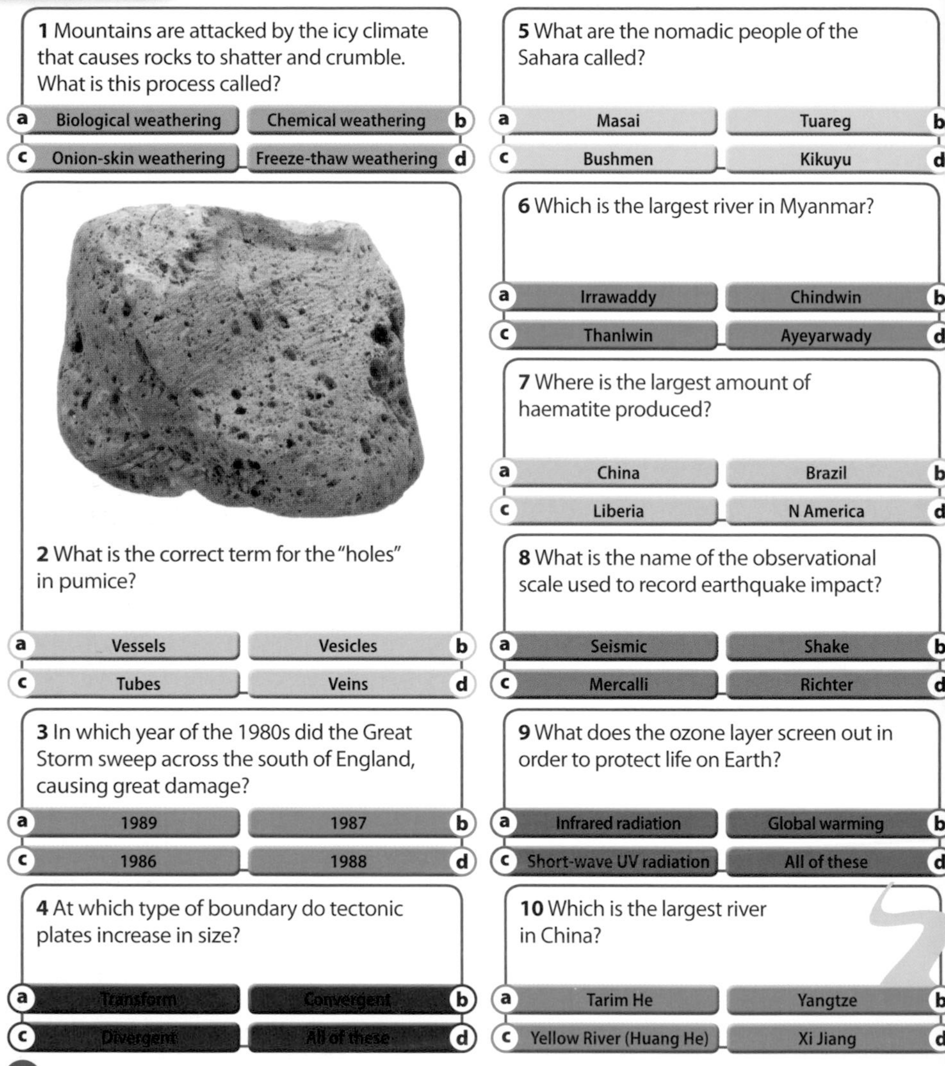

2 What is the correct term for the "holes" in pumice?

- a Vessels
- b Vesicles
- c Tubes
- d Veins

3 In which year of the 1980s did the Great Storm sweep across the south of England, causing great damage?

- a 1989
- b 1987
- c 1986
- d 1988

4 At which type of boundary do tectonic plates increase in size?

- a Transform
- b Convergent
- c Divergent
- d All of these

5 What are the nomadic people of the Sahara called?

- a Masai
- b Tuareg
- c Bushmen
- d Kikuyu

6 Which is the largest river in Myanmar?

- a Irrawaddy
- b Chindwin
- c Thanlwin
- d Ayeyarwady

7 Where is the largest amount of haematite produced?

- a China
- b Brazil
- c Liberia
- d N America

8 What is the name of the observational scale used to record earthquake impact?

- a Seismic
- b Shake
- c Mercalli
- d Richter

9 What does the ozone layer screen out in order to protect life on Earth?

- a Infrared radiation
- b Global warming
- c Short-wave UV radiation
- d All of these

10 Which is the largest river in China?

- a Tarim He
- b Yangtze
- c Yellow River (Huang He)
- d Xi Jiang

11 Which of the following is not a limestone?

- a Shelly
- b Pisolitic
- c Micaceous
- d Crinoidal

12 How many sides do almost all snowflakes have?

- a 6
- b 5
- c 7
- d 10

13 How deep is the deepest point of an ocean?

- a Just under 5km (3 miles)
- b Nearly 11km (7 miles)
- c About 6km (4 miles)
- d 16km (10 miles)

14 Which is the most northerly sea in the Atlantic?

- a North Sea
- b Baltic Sea
- c White Sea
- d Norwegian Sea

15 In which country are the world's deepest mines?

- a S Africa
- b Wales
- c Chile
- d China

16 Where would you find a rain shadow?

- a Under a cumulus cloud
- b At a cold front
- c Over large lakes
- d Lee side of a mountain

17 Whirlpools form alongside powerful tidal currents. Where is the world's largest whirlpool?

- a Corryvreckan, UK
- b Saltstraumen, Norway
- c Maelstrom, Norway
- d Old Sow, Canada

18 When did the first signs of life on Earth appear?

- a 3.8 billion years ago
- b 4.2 billion years ago
- c 3 billion years ago
- d 2.5 billion years ago

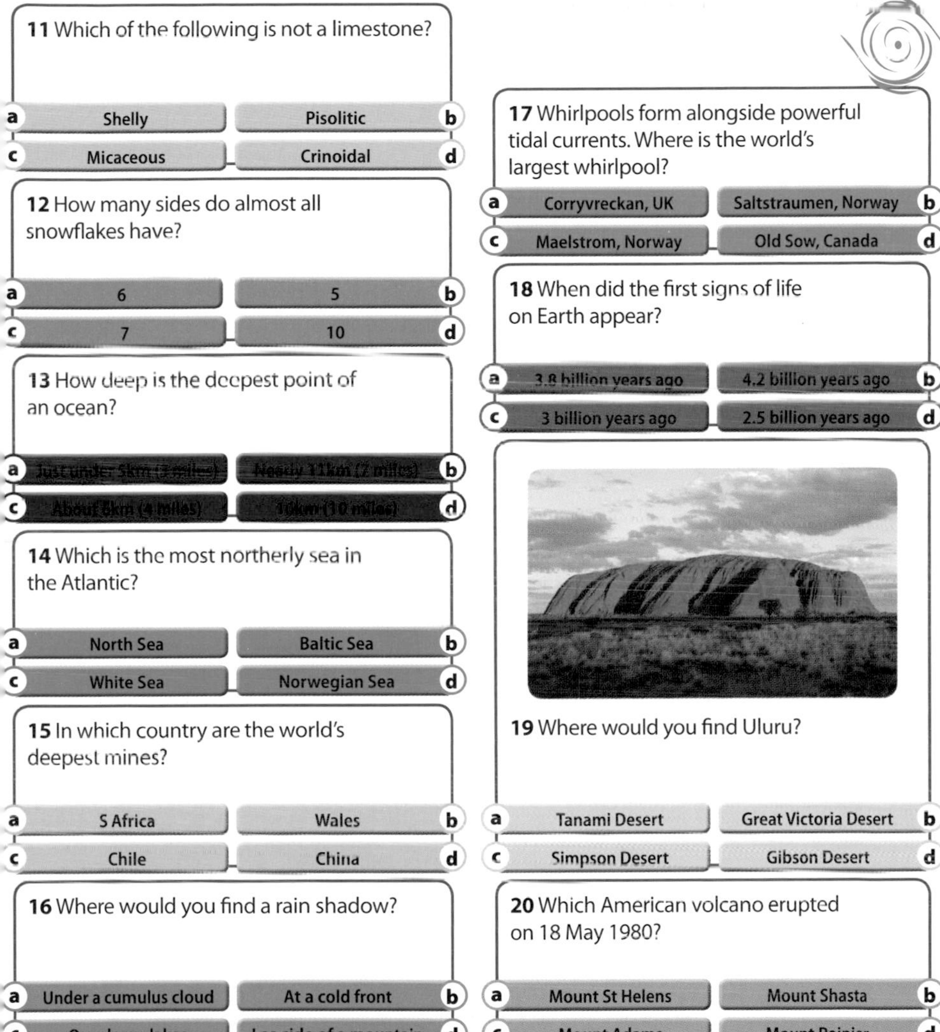

19 Where would you find Uluru?

- a Tanami Desert
- b Great Victoria Desert
- c Simpson Desert
- d Gibson Desert

20 Which American volcano erupted on 18 May 1980?

- a Mount St Helens
- b Mount Shasta
- c Mount Adams
- d Mount Rainier

Quiz **18**

A 60-tonne **meteorite** from Namibia

1 At what sort of speed can a tsunami wave travel?

a Up to 400kph (249mph)
b Up to 620kph (385mph)
c Up to 800kph (497mph)
d Up to 250kph (155mph)

2 In which country is Lake Volta?

a Sierra Leone
b Liberia
c Mali
d Ghana

3 Which ocean trench runs southwest off the Kamchatka Peninsula?

a Aleutian Trench
b Cayman Trench
c Java Trench
d Kuril Trench

4 Which N American mountain range extends from Quebec to northern Alabama?

a Appalachians
b Rocky Mountains
c Adirondacks
d Baffin Mountains

5 Which gemstone has a hardness of 8 on the Mohs' scale?

a Topaz
b Diamond
c Talc
d Gypsum

6 Which type of glacier is Alaska's Aletsch Glacier?

a Outlet
b Cirque
c Valley
d Piedmont

7 What is distinctive about cirrostratus clouds?

a High and sheet-like
b Low and puffy
c High and very white
d High and wispy

8 Linear dunes are characteristic of which desert?

a Nubian
b Kalahari
c Sahara
d Namib

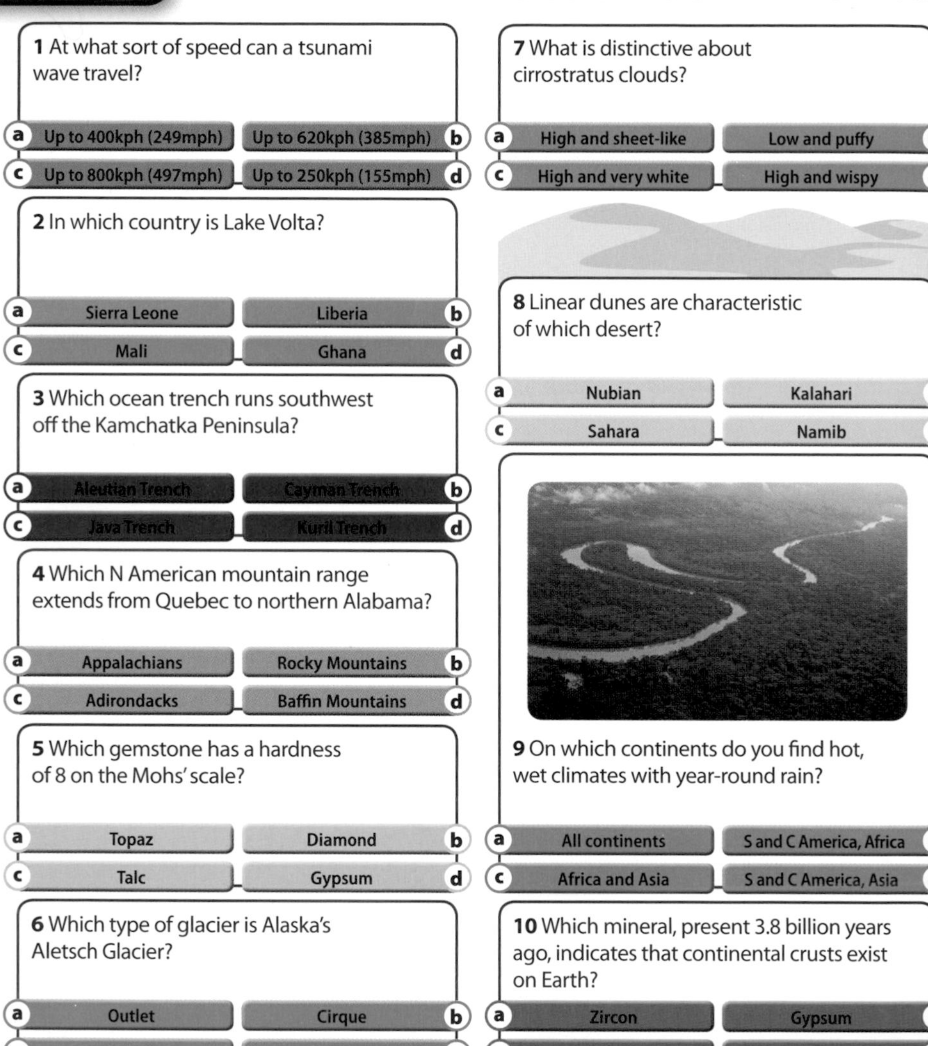

9 On which continents do you find hot, wet climates with year-round rain?

a All continents
b S and C America, Africa
c Africa and Asia
d S and C America, Asia

10 Which mineral, present 3.8 billion years ago, indicates that continental crusts exist on Earth?

a Zircon
b Gypsum
c Calcite
d Talc

11 The Iapetus Ocean could be said to be a precursor of which present-day ocean?

a Indian Ocean
b Arctic Ocean
c Atlantic Ocean
d Pacific Ocean

12 What makes fog different to mist?

a Pollution levels
b Temperature
c Density
d All of these

13 About how many meteorites strike Earth each year?

a 1,000
b 750
c 500
d 20

14 Which sill runs along the west side of the River Hudson in New York?

a Fair Head Sill
b Whin Sill
c Mackenzie Dykes
d Palisades

15 The end of a glacier can be called a…

a Snout
b Nose
c Exit
d Mouth

16 What should you be able to scratch a mineral with, if that mineral has a hardness of one?

a Knife
b Glass
c Fingernail
d Graphite pencil

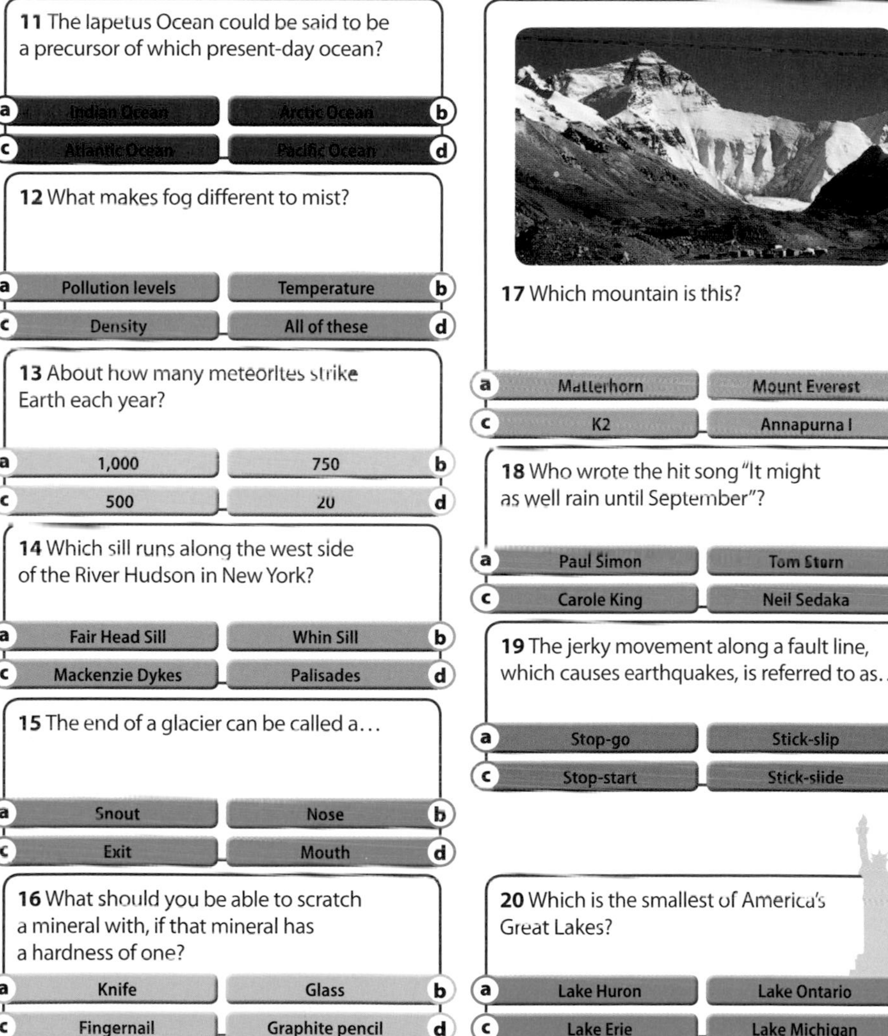

17 Which mountain is this?

a Matterhorn
b Mount Everest
c K2
d Annapurna I

18 Who wrote the hit song "It might as well rain until September"?

a Paul Simon
b Tom Stern
c Carole King
d Neil Sedaka

19 The jerky movement along a fault line, which causes earthquakes, is referred to as…

a Stop-go
b Stick-slip
c Stop-start
d Stick-slide

20 Which is the smallest of America's Great Lakes?

a Lake Huron
b Lake Ontario
c Lake Erie
d Lake Michigan

Angel Falls in Venezuela is the world's

1 Earth's crust is divided into huge plates that float on the hot rock below. When these move, what can happen?

a Volcanoes | b Continents move
c Earthquakes | d All of these

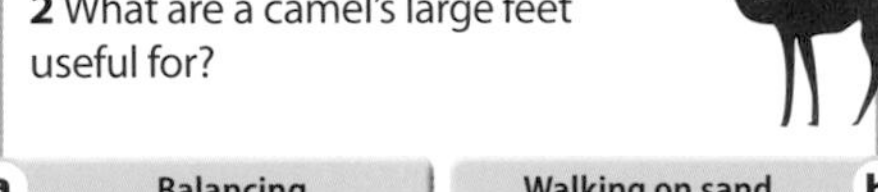

2 What are a camel's large feet useful for?

a Balancing | b Walking on sand
c Keeping cool | d Digging

3 On which river does Paris lie?

a Eiffel | b Oise
c Loire | d Seine

4 Which of these is not a physical property of minerals?

a Chemical composition | b Colour
c Hardness | d Crystal shape

5 What falls from the sky at 140kph (87mph) and can weigh up to 1kg (2lb)?

a Lightning bolt | b Hailstone
c Snowflake | d Raindrop

6 Movement along which fault led to the 1989 earthquake in San Francisco?

a Denali | b San Andreas
c New Madrid | d Eagle Bay

7 Which group of minerals includes gold?

a Phosphates | b Silicates
c Carbonates | d Native elements

8 Which term is used to describe a river of ice flowing from snowcapped mountains?

a Ice sheet | b Snowfield
c Frozen flow | d Glacier

9 What is the outer layer of Earth, which is made up of tectonic plates, called?

- **a** Lithosphere
- **b** Biosphere
- **c** Hydrosphere
- **d** Atmosphere

10 Which of the following countries does not cross into the Arctic Circle?

- **a** Iceland
- **b** Norway
- **c** Russia
- **d** Greenland

11 This mountain has the faces of four presidents carved into it. What is its name?

- **a** Mount Lincoln
- **b** Mount Sherman
- **c** Mount Rushmore
- **d** Mount Rainier

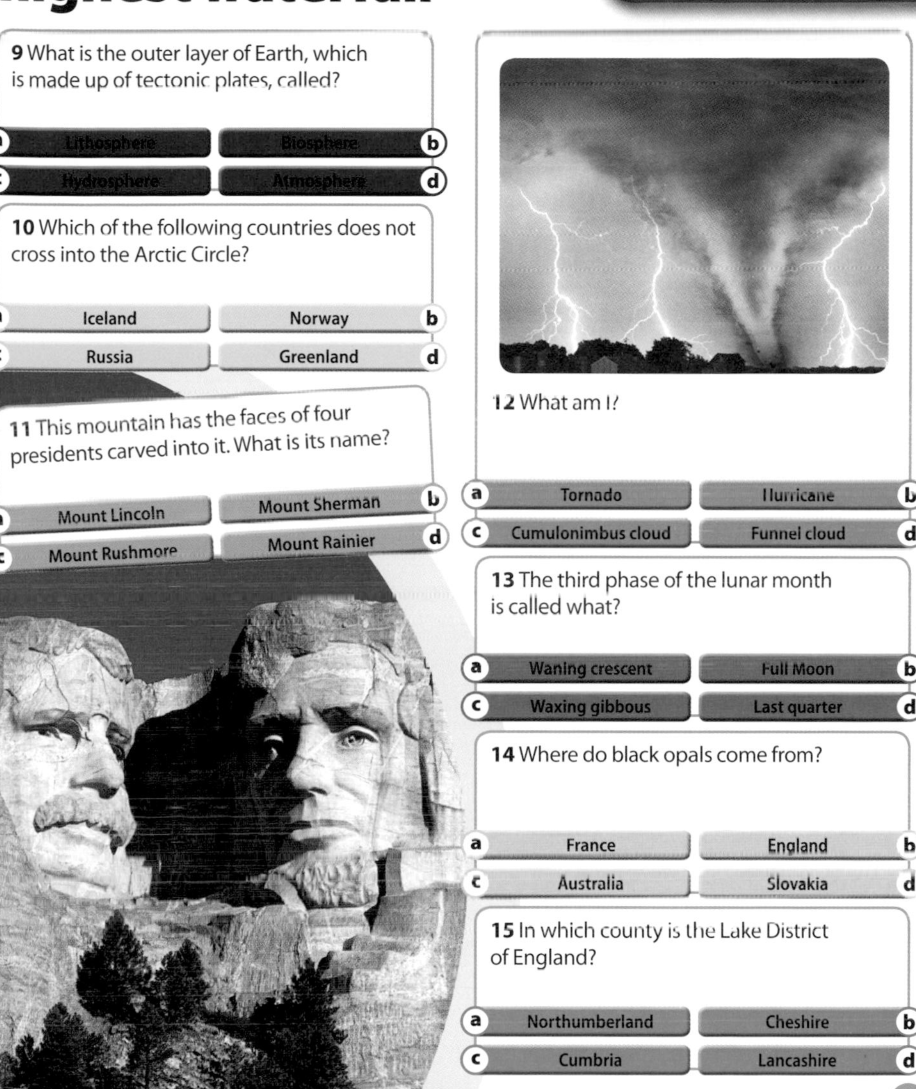

12 What am I?

- **a** Tornado
- **b** Hurricane
- **c** Cumulonimbus cloud
- **d** Funnel cloud

13 The third phase of the lunar month is called what?

- **a** Waning crescent
- **b** Full Moon
- **c** Waxing gibbous
- **d** Last quarter

14 Where do black opals come from?

- **a** France
- **b** England
- **c** Australia
- **d** Slovakia

15 In which county is the Lake District of England?

- **a** Northumberland
- **b** Cheshire
- **c** Cumbria
- **d** Lancashire

The name **Australia** comes from the

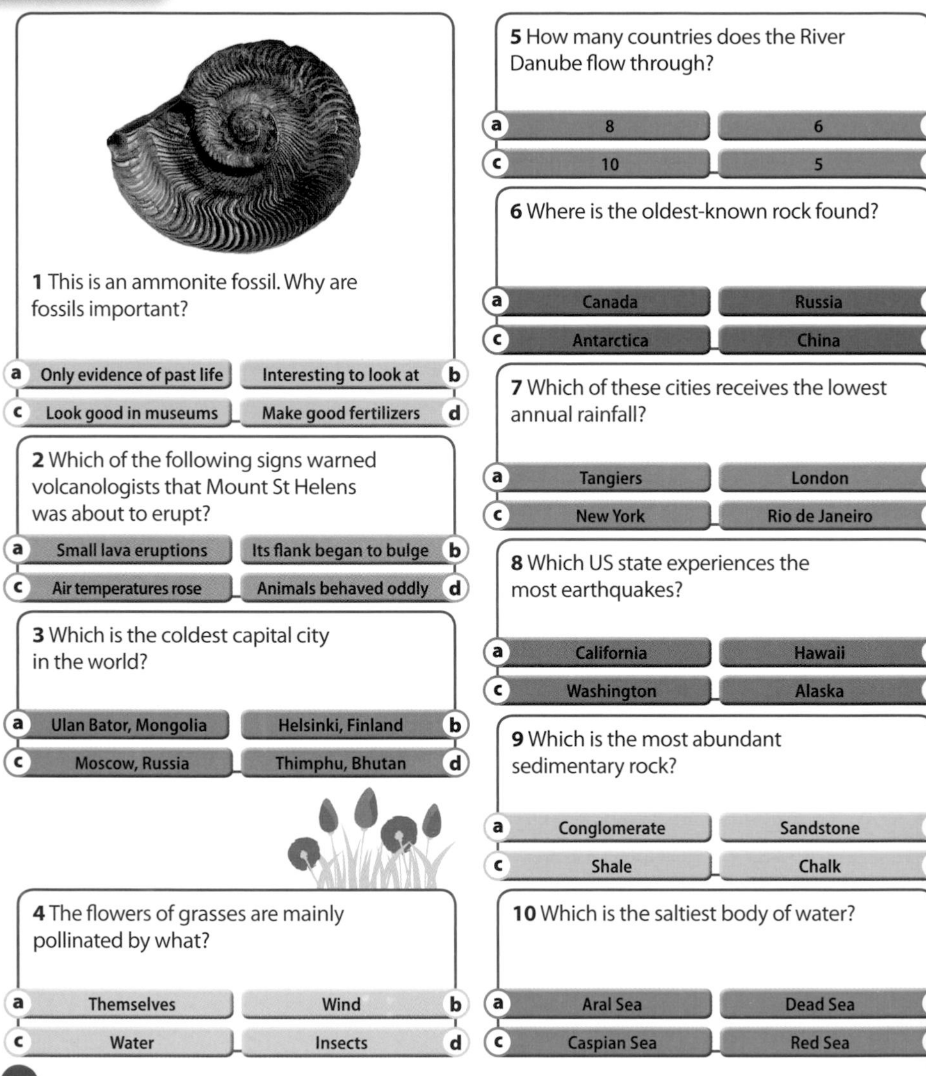

1 This is an ammonite fossil. Why are fossils important?

- a Only evidence of past life
- b Interesting to look at
- c Look good in museums
- d Make good fertilizers

2 Which of the following signs warned volcanologists that Mount St Helens was about to erupt?

- a Small lava eruptions
- b Its flank began to bulge
- c Air temperatures rose
- d Animals behaved oddly

3 Which is the coldest capital city in the world?

- a Ulan Bator, Mongolia
- b Helsinki, Finland
- c Moscow, Russia
- d Thimphu, Bhutan

4 The flowers of grasses are mainly pollinated by what?

- a Themselves
- b Wind
- c Water
- d Insects

5 How many countries does the River Danube flow through?

- a 8
- b 6
- c 10
- d 5

6 Where is the oldest-known rock found?

- a Canada
- b Russia
- c Antarctica
- d China

7 Which of these cities receives the lowest annual rainfall?

- a Tangiers
- b London
- c New York
- d Rio de Janeiro

8 Which US state experiences the most earthquakes?

- a California
- b Hawaii
- c Washington
- d Alaska

9 Which is the most abundant sedimentary rock?

- a Conglomerate
- b Sandstone
- c Shale
- d Chalk

10 Which is the saltiest body of water?

- a Aral Sea
- b Dead Sea
- c Caspian Sea
- d Red Sea

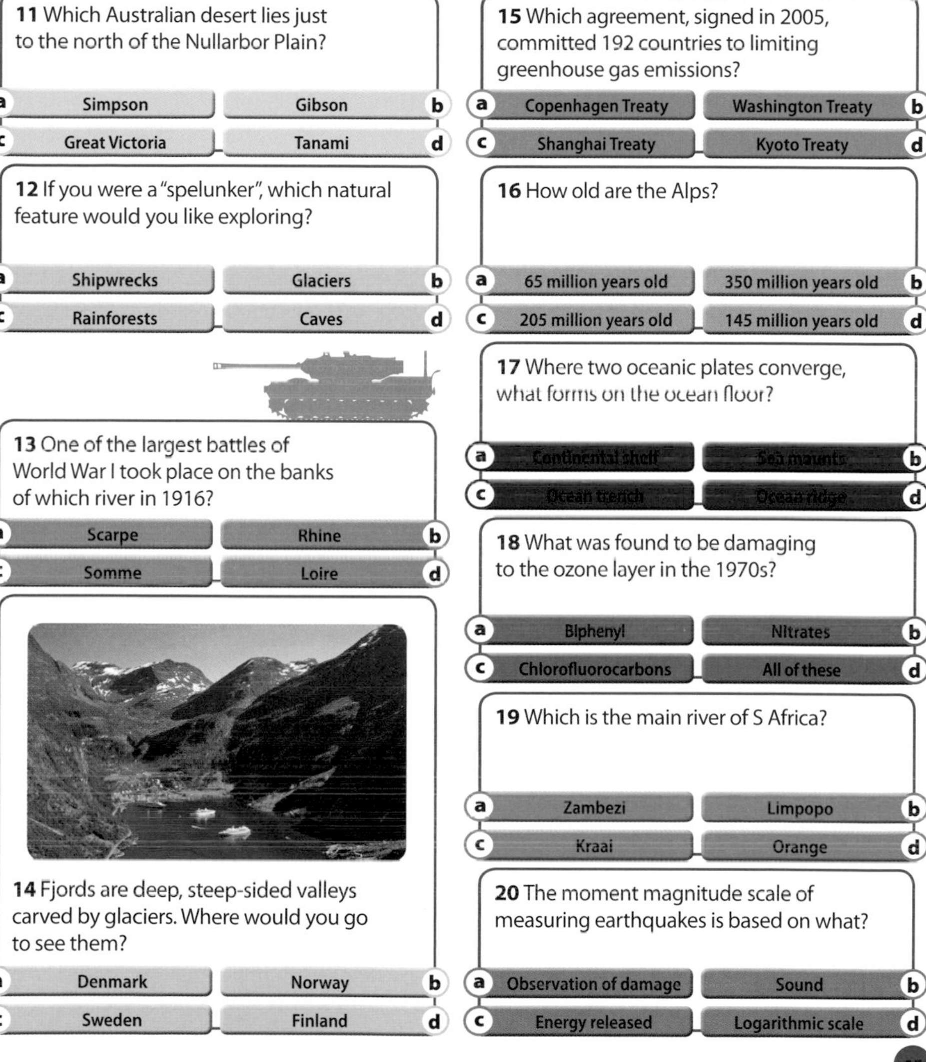

11 Which Australian desert lies just to the north of the Nullarbor Plain?

a Simpson
b Gibson
c Great Victoria
d Tanami

12 If you were a "spelunker", which natural feature would you like exploring?

a Shipwrecks
b Glaciers
c Rainforests
d Caves

13 One of the largest battles of World War I took place on the banks of which river in 1916?

a Scarpe
b Rhine
c Somme
d Loire

14 Fjords are deep, steep-sided valleys carved by glaciers. Where would you go to see them?

a Denmark
b Norway
c Sweden
d Finland

15 Which agreement, signed in 2005, committed 192 countries to limiting greenhouse gas emissions?

a Copenhagen Treaty
b Washington Treaty
c Shanghai Treaty
d Kyoto Treaty

16 How old are the Alps?

a 65 million years old
b 350 million years old
c 205 million years old
d 145 million years old

17 Where two oceanic plates converge, what forms on the ocean floor?

a Continental shelf
b Sea mounts
c Ocean trench
d Ocean ridge

18 What was found to be damaging to the ozone layer in the 1970s?

a Biphenyl
b Nitrates
c Chlorofluorocarbons
d All of these

19 Which is the main river of S Africa?

a Zambezi
b Limpopo
c Kraai
d Orange

20 The moment magnitude scale of measuring earthquakes is based on what?

a Observation of damage
b Sound
c Energy released
d Logarithmic scale

21

Coral reefs are home to 25 per cent

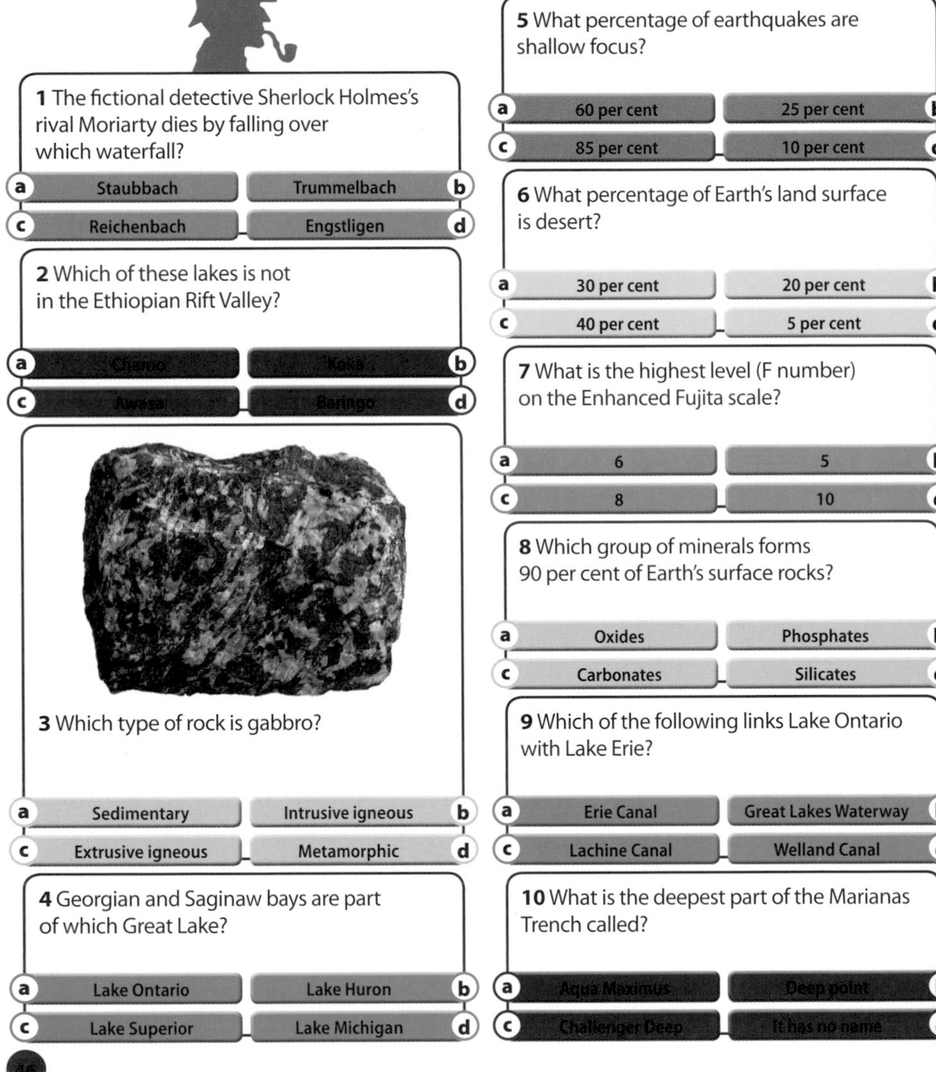

1 The fictional detective Sherlock Holmes's rival Moriarty dies by falling over which waterfall?

- a Staubbach
- b Trummelbach
- c Reichenbach
- d Engstligen

2 Which of these lakes is not in the Ethiopian Rift Valley?

- a Chamo
- b Koka
- c Awasa
- d Baringo

3 Which type of rock is gabbro?

- a Sedimentary
- b Intrusive igneous
- c Extrusive igneous
- d Metamorphic

4 Georgian and Saginaw bays are part of which Great Lake?

- a Lake Ontario
- b Lake Huron
- c Lake Superior
- d Lake Michigan

5 What percentage of earthquakes are shallow focus?

- a 60 per cent
- b 25 per cent
- c 85 per cent
- d 10 per cent

6 What percentage of Earth's land surface is desert?

- a 30 per cent
- b 20 per cent
- c 40 per cent
- d 5 per cent

7 What is the highest level (F number) on the Enhanced Fujita scale?

- a 6
- b 5
- c 8
- d 10

8 Which group of minerals forms 90 per cent of Earth's surface rocks?

- a Oxides
- b Phosphates
- c Carbonates
- d Silicates

9 Which of the following links Lake Ontario with Lake Erie?

- a Erie Canal
- b Great Lakes Waterway
- c Lachine Canal
- d Welland Canal

10 What is the deepest part of the Marianas Trench called?

- a Aqua Maximus
- b Deep point
- c Challenger Deep
- d It has no name

of all marine **fish** species

11 Which of these mountain ranges has large accumulations of platinum?

- a Urals
- b Alps
- c Jura
- d Scandinavian

12 Which of the following is not a type of wind?

- a Mistral
- b Sirocco
- c Chinook
- d Haboob

13 A tsunami can have a wavelength of more than…

- a 200km (124 miles)
- b 1,000km (621 miles)
- c 700km (435 miles)
- d 500km (311 miles)

14 Part of which mountain range forms the eastern border of Lesotho?

- a Outeniqua
- b Drakensberg
- c Cederberg
- d Swartberg

15 Which UK Met Office shipping forecast area lies immediately north of the Irish Sea?

- a Rockall
- b Bailey
- c Malin
- d Hebrides

16 What percentage of meteorites are iron meteorites?

- a 55 per cent
- b 85 per cent
- c 5 per cent
- d 25 per cent

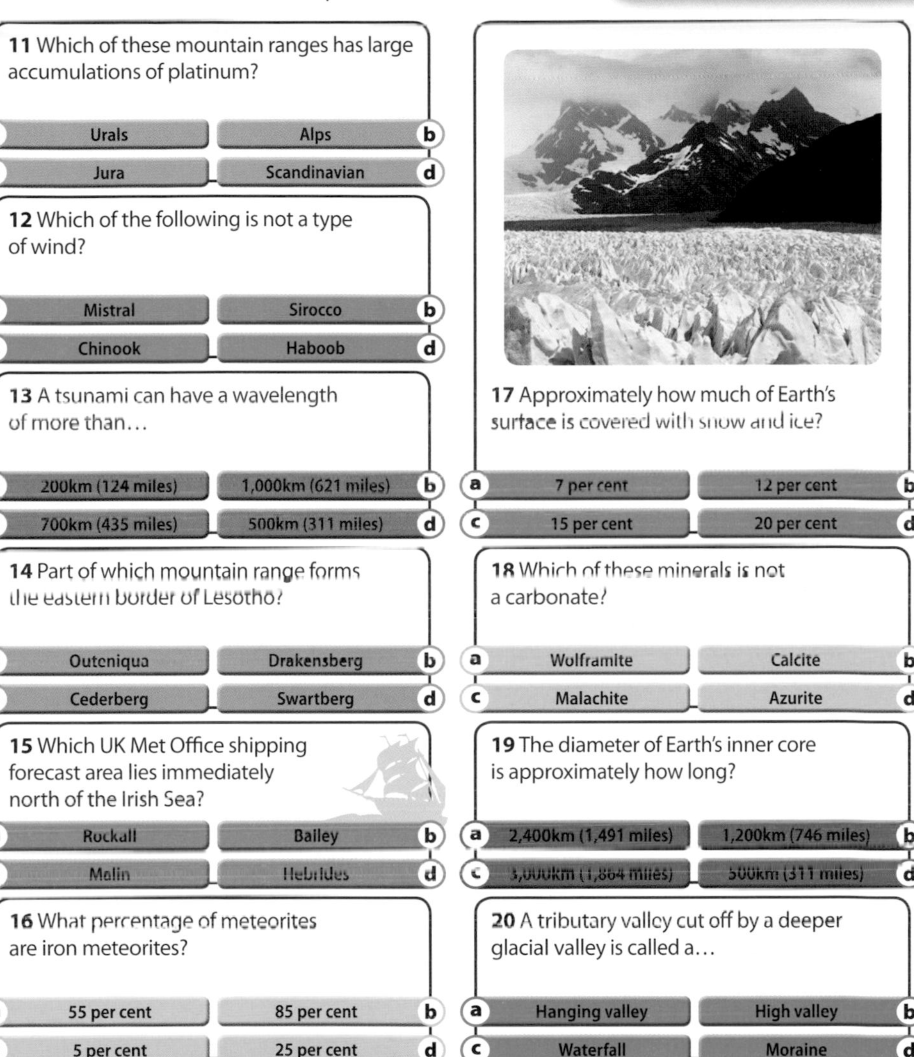

17 Approximately how much of Earth's surface is covered with snow and ice?

- a 7 per cent
- b 12 per cent
- c 15 per cent
- d 20 per cent

18 Which of these minerals is not a carbonate?

- a Wolframite
- b Calcite
- c Malachite
- d Azurite

19 The diameter of Earth's inner core is approximately how long?

- a 2,400km (1,491 miles)
- b 1,200km (746 miles)
- c 3,000km (1,864 miles)
- d 500km (311 miles)

20 A tributary valley cut off by a deeper glacial valley is called a…

- a Hanging valley
- b High valley
- c Waterfall
- d Moraine

The **youngest** person to climb

1 Which of these is caused by global warming?

- a Melting of ice sheets
- b More extreme weather
- c Rising sea levels
- d All of these

2 What is the name given to the laying down of rock-forming sediments?

- a Intrusion
- b Weathering
- c Grading
- d Deposition

3 Which of the following plates does not have a large continental landmass on it?

- a Eurasian
- b Pacific
- c S American
- d African

4 Which is the second-highest mountain on Earth?

- a K2
- b Annapurna I
- c Mont Blanc
- d Ben Nevis

5 Which of these thrives in lowland areas with hot, wet climates?

- a Coniferous forest
- b Deciduous forest
- c Tropical rainforest
- d Grass

6 Which fictional mineral had a detrimental effect on Superman?

- a Kryptonite
- b Lutherite
- c Joelite
- d Kandorite

7 All deserts are…

- a Sandy
- b Uninhabited
- c Dry
- d Hot

8 Who set out to find the source of the Nile in 1866?

- a Henry Stanley
- b Gerard Way
- c Gustav Nachtigal
- d David Livingstone

9 Approximately how old is Earth?

a 450 million years
b 450,000 years
c 450 years
d 4.5 billion years

10 Earthquakes are not associated with which of the following?

a Tectonic plates
b Volcanoes
c Glaciation
d Faults

11 In which rainforest would you find this ruffed lemur?

a Amazonian
b Madagascan
c Central African
d Indonesian

12 Which mountains were created when the landmass of India collided with Eurasia?

a Alps
b Rocky Mountains
c Appalachians
d Himalayas

13 Which of the following is a carbonate mineral?

a Galena
b Calcite
c Borax
d Mica

14 Earth appears blue from space because of…

a Light
b Ice
c Water
d Land

15 Which is the world's longest river?

a Nile
b Amazon
c Ganges
d Danube

Quiz **23**

Only **22 per cent** of the

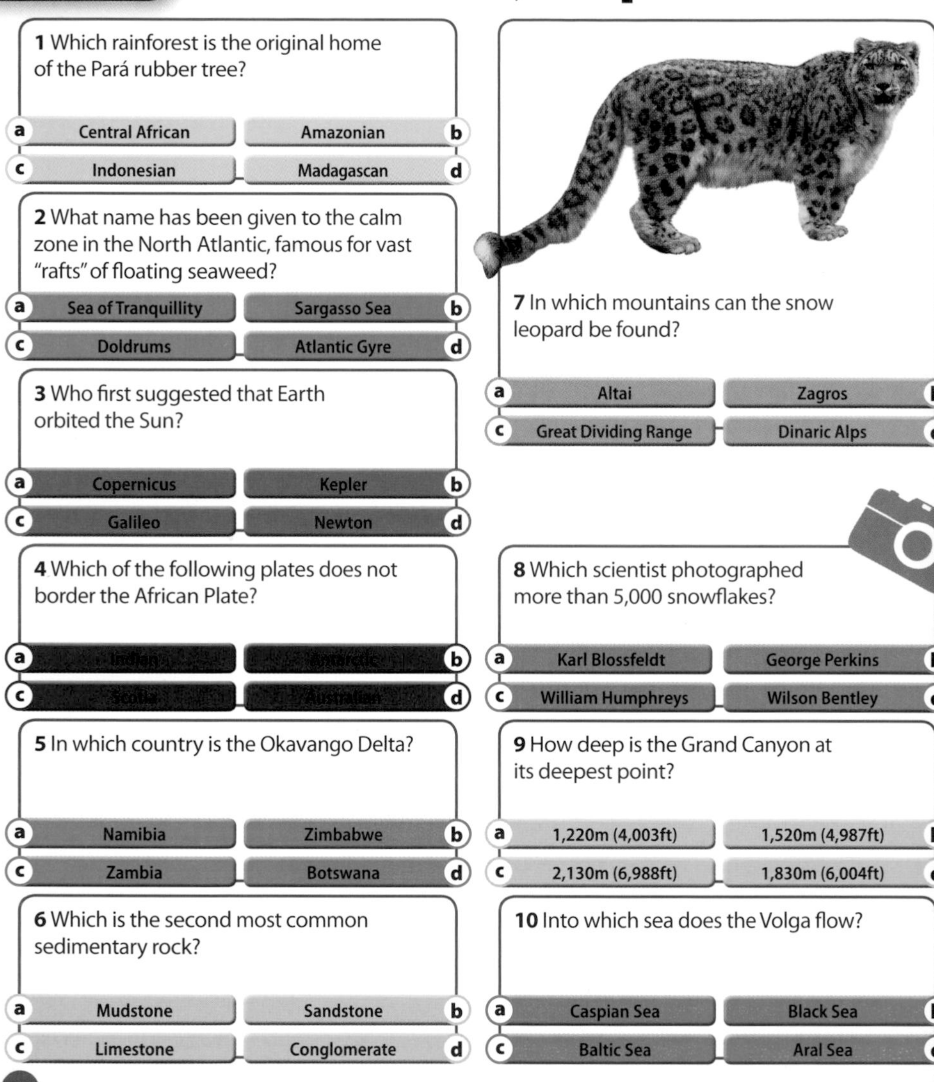

1 Which rainforest is the original home of the Pará rubber tree?

a Central African
b Amazonian
c Indonesian
d Madagascan

2 What name has been given to the calm zone in the North Atlantic, famous for vast "rafts" of floating seaweed?

a Sea of Tranquillity
b Sargasso Sea
c Doldrums
d Atlantic Gyre

3 Who first suggested that Earth orbited the Sun?

a Copernicus
b Kepler
c Galileo
d Newton

4 Which of the following plates does not border the African Plate?

a Indian
b Antarctic
c Scotia
d Australian

5 In which country is the Okavango Delta?

a Namibia
b Zimbabwe
c Zambia
d Botswana

6 Which is the second most common sedimentary rock?

a Mudstone
b Sandstone
c Limestone
d Conglomerate

7 In which mountains can the snow leopard be found?

a Altai
b Zagros
c Great Dividing Range
d Dinaric Alps

8 Which scientist photographed more than 5,000 snowflakes?

a Karl Blossfeldt
b George Perkins
c William Humphreys
d Wilson Bentley

9 How deep is the Grand Canyon at its deepest point?

a 1,220m (4,003ft)
b 1,520m (4,987ft)
c 2,130m (6,988ft)
d 1,830m (6,004ft)

10 Into which sea does the Volga flow?

a Caspian Sea
b Black Sea
c Baltic Sea
d Aral Sea

River Nile is in Egypt

Difficulty level: **Medium**

11 Which natural hazard is measured on the Saffir–Simpson scale, with 5 being the highest value?

- a Hurricane
- b Tornado
- c Wave height
- d Volcanic eruption

12 Where are most transform faults found?

- a Under glaciers
- b On the ocean floor
- c Along the coast
- d In mountains

13 Which is the most northerly sea in the Pacific?

- a Sea of Japan
- b Yellow Sea
- c Bering Sea
- d Sea of Okhotsk

14 Ozone can be found dangerously close to the ground. What might cause it to occur there naturally?

- a Hail
- b Tornado
- c Earthquake
- d Lightning

15 The heavily eroded Caledonian mountains of Scotland were once as tall as the Himalayas. How old are they?

- a 1 billion years old
- b 500 million years old
- c 400 million years old
- d 250 million years old

16 The fastest type of seismic wave is known by which letter?

- a H
- b P
- c S
- d X

17 What is three-quarters of all gypsum mined used to make?

- a Fertilizer
- b Paint pigments
- c Plaster of Paris
- d Cement

18 Which term is used to describe a volcano that rarely erupts?

- a Extinct
- b Active
- c Waiting
- d Dormant

19 What is the scientific study of weather called?

- a Seismology
- b Astrology
- c Meteorology
- d Cosmology

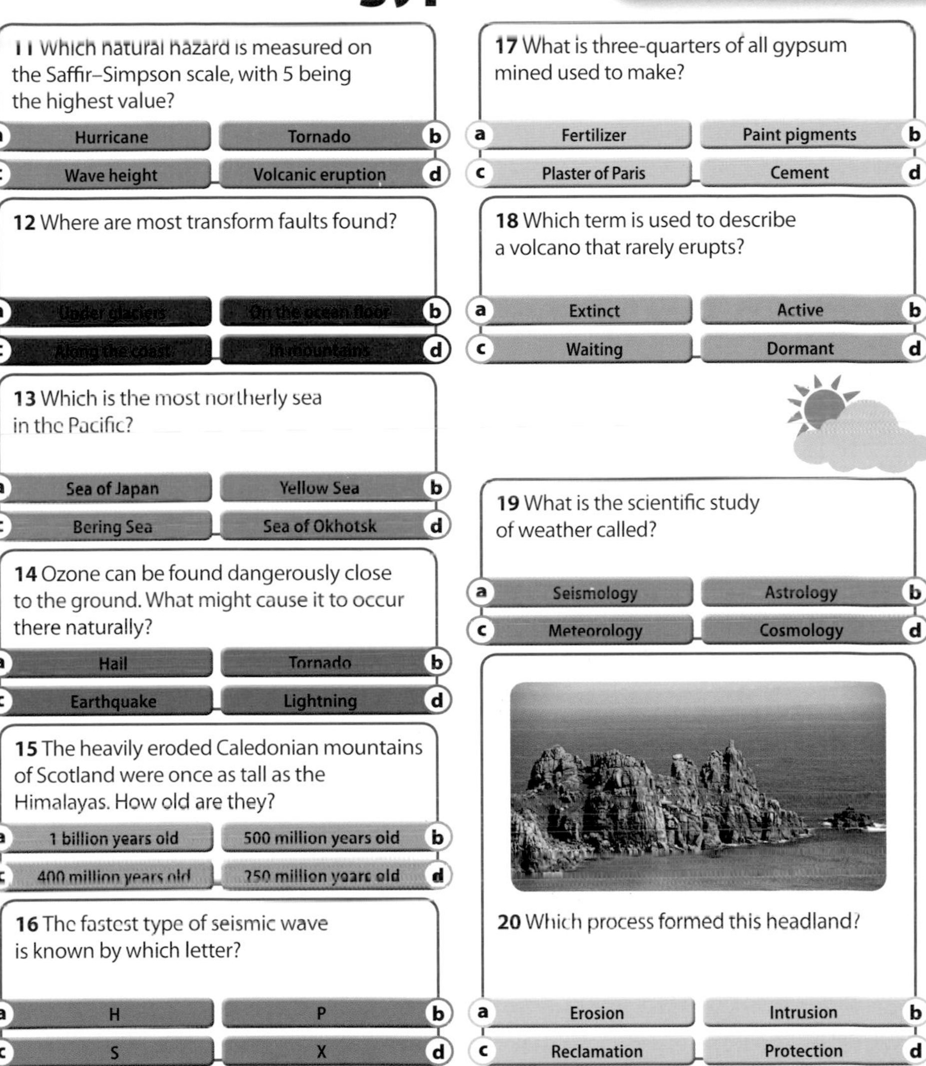

20 Which process formed this headland?

- a Erosion
- b Intrusion
- c Reclamation
- d Protection

Tectonic plates fit together

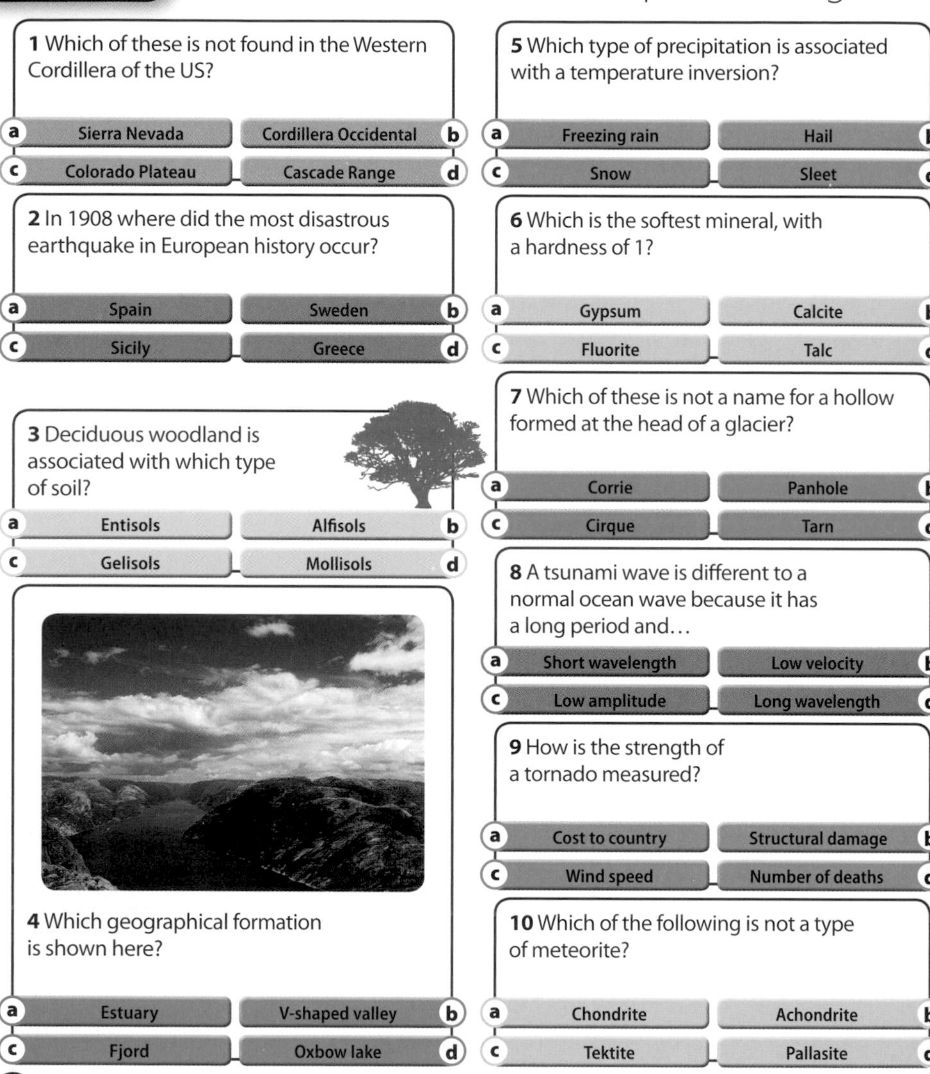

1 Which of these is not found in the Western Cordillera of the US?

a Sierra Nevada
b Cordillera Occidental
c Colorado Plateau
d Cascade Range

2 In 1908 where did the most disastrous earthquake in European history occur?

a Spain
b Sweden
c Sicily
d Greece

3 Deciduous woodland is associated with which type of soil?

a Entisols
b Alfisols
c Gelisols
d Mollisols

4 Which geographical formation is shown here?

a Estuary
b V-shaped valley
c Fjord
d Oxbow lake

5 Which type of precipitation is associated with a temperature inversion?

a Freezing rain
b Hail
c Snow
d Sleet

6 Which is the softest mineral, with a hardness of 1?

a Gypsum
b Calcite
c Fluorite
d Talc

7 Which of these is not a name for a hollow formed at the head of a glacier?

a Corrie
b Panhole
c Cirque
d Tarn

8 A tsunami wave is different to a normal ocean wave because it has a long period and…

a Short wavelength
b Low velocity
c Low amplitude
d Long wavelength

9 How is the strength of a tornado measured?

a Cost to country
b Structural damage
c Wind speed
d Number of deaths

10 Which of the following is not a type of meteorite?

a Chondrite
b Achondrite
c Tektite
d Pallasite

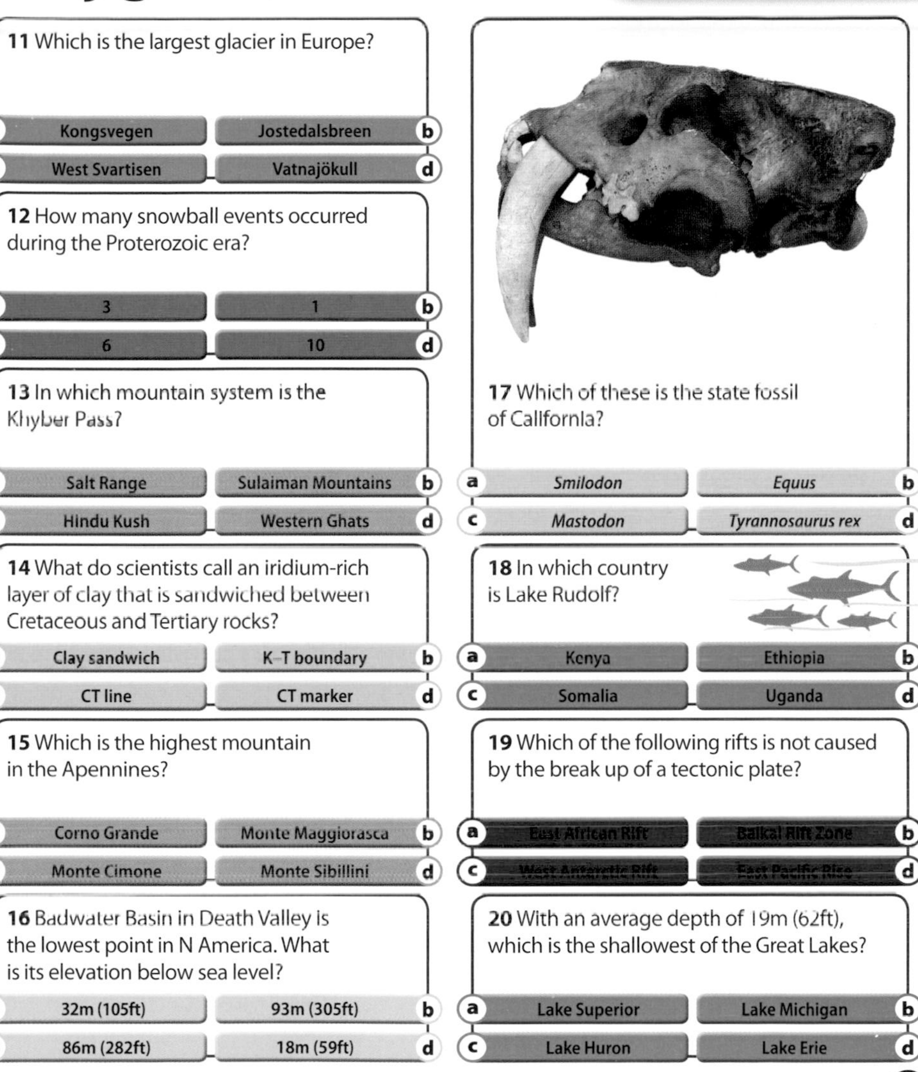

11 Which is the largest glacier in Europe?

- a Kongsvegen
- b Jostedalsbreen
- c West Svartisen
- d Vatnajökull

12 How many snowball events occurred during the Proterozoic era?

- a 3
- b 1
- c 6
- d 10

13 In which mountain system is the Khyber Pass?

- a Salt Range
- b Sulaiman Mountains
- c Hindu Kush
- d Western Ghats

14 What do scientists call an iridium-rich layer of clay that is sandwiched between Cretaceous and Tertiary rocks?

- a Clay sandwich
- b K–T boundary
- c CT line
- d CT marker

15 Which is the highest mountain in the Apennines?

- a Corno Grande
- b Monte Maggiorasca
- c Monte Cimone
- d Monte Sibillini

16 Badwater Basin in Death Valley is the lowest point in N America. What is its elevation below sea level?

- a 32m (105ft)
- b 93m (305ft)
- c 86m (282ft)
- d 18m (59ft)

17 Which of these is the state fossil of California?

- a *Smilodon*
- b *Equus*
- c *Mastodon*
- d *Tyrannosaurus rex*

18 In which country is Lake Rudolf?

- a Kenya
- b Ethiopia
- c Somalia
- d Uganda

19 Which of the following rifts is not caused by the break up of a tectonic plate?

- a East African Rift
- b Baikal Rift Zone
- c West Antarctic Rift
- d East Pacific Rise

20 With an average depth of 19m (62ft), which is the shallowest of the Great Lakes?

- a Lake Superior
- b Lake Michigan
- c Lake Huron
- d Lake Erie

In 1815 an **eruption** in Indonesia

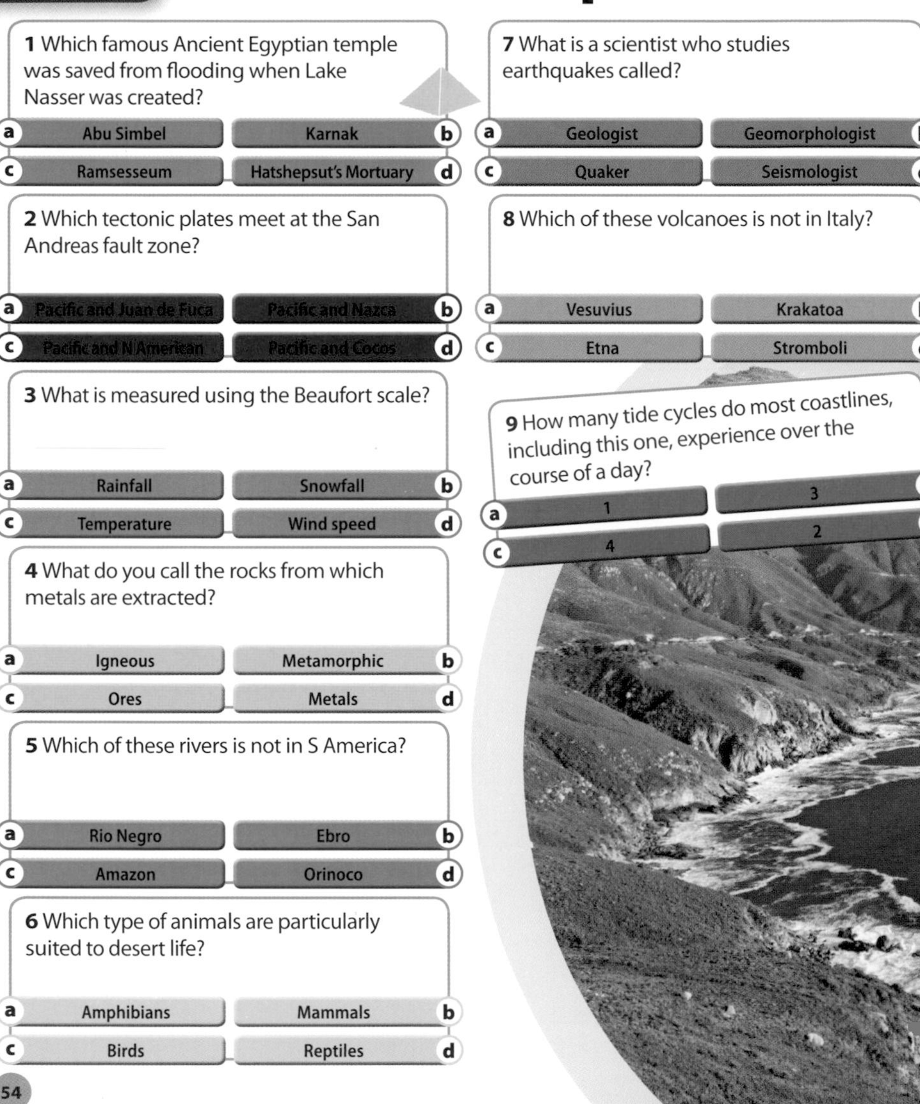

1 Which famous Ancient Egyptian temple was saved from flooding when Lake Nasser was created?

a Abu Simbel
b Karnak
c Ramsesseum
d Hatshepsut's Mortuary

2 Which tectonic plates meet at the San Andreas fault zone?

a Pacific and Juan de Fuca
b Pacific and Nazca
c Pacific and N American
d Pacific and Cocos

3 What is measured using the Beaufort scale?

a Rainfall
b Snowfall
c Temperature
d Wind speed

4 What do you call the rocks from which metals are extracted?

a Igneous
b Metamorphic
c Ores
d Metals

5 Which of these rivers is not in S America?

a Rio Negro
b Ebro
c Amazon
d Orinoco

6 Which type of animals are particularly suited to desert life?

a Amphibians
b Mammals
c Birds
d Reptiles

7 What is a scientist who studies earthquakes called?

a Geologist
b Geomorphologist
c Quaker
d Seismologist

8 Which of these volcanoes is not in Italy?

a Vesuvius
b Krakatoa
c Etna
d Stromboli

9 How many tide cycles do most coastlines, including this one, experience over the course of a day?

a 1
b 3
c 4
d 2

10 The Arctic Circle crosses three continents. How many continents does the Antarctic Circle cross?

a 3 | b 2
c 1 | d None

11 Which of the following is not a type of metamorphism?

a Glacial | b Contact
c Regional | d Dynamic

12 This mountain range forms the border between France and Spain. What is it called?

a Pyrenees | b Carpathians
c Urals | d Himalayas

13 Which of the following is not one of Earth's layers?

a Outer mantle | b Inner core
c Upper mantle | d Crust

14 During the rock cycle, uplift of rocks leads to what?

a Erosion | b Weathering
c Exposure | d All of these

15 Which of the following has a warm, temperate climate?

a Minnesota | b New Mexico
c California | d New York

Quiz 26

Antarctica is the **highest**, driest,

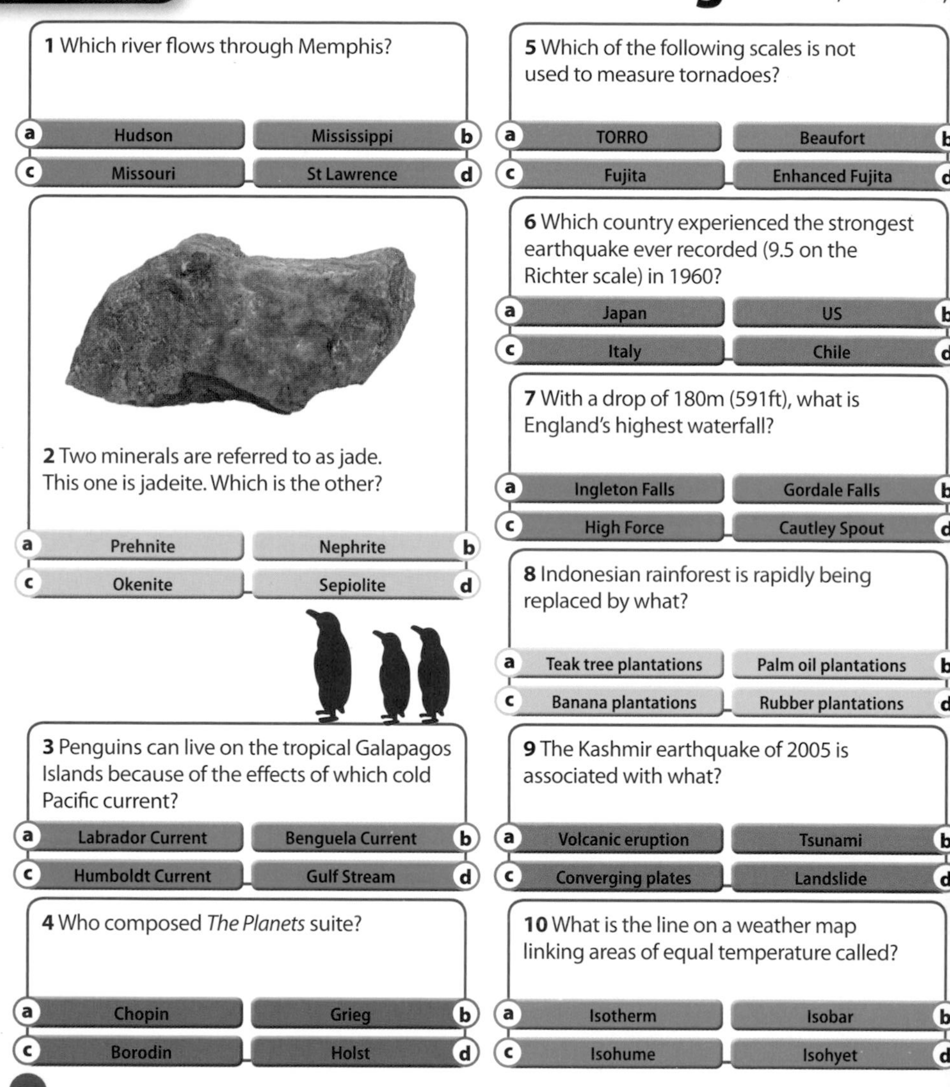

1 Which river flows through Memphis?

a Hudson
b Mississippi
c Missouri
d St Lawrence

2 Two minerals are referred to as jade. This one is jadeite. Which is the other?

a Prehnite
b Nephrite
c Okenite
d Sepiolite

3 Penguins can live on the tropical Galapagos Islands because of the effects of which cold Pacific current?

a Labrador Current
b Benguela Current
c Humboldt Current
d Gulf Stream

4 Who composed *The Planets* suite?

a Chopin
b Grieg
c Borodin
d Holst

5 Which of the following scales is not used to measure tornadoes?

a TORRO
b Beaufort
c Fujita
d Enhanced Fujita

6 Which country experienced the strongest earthquake ever recorded (9.5 on the Richter scale) in 1960?

a Japan
b US
c Italy
d Chile

7 With a drop of 180m (591ft), what is England's highest waterfall?

a Ingleton Falls
b Gordale Falls
c High Force
d Cautley Spout

8 Indonesian rainforest is rapidly being replaced by what?

a Teak tree plantations
b Palm oil plantations
c Banana plantations
d Rubber plantations

9 The Kashmir earthquake of 2005 is associated with what?

a Volcanic eruption
b Tsunami
c Converging plates
d Landslide

10 What is the line on a weather map linking areas of equal temperature called?

a Isotherm
b Isobar
c Isohume
d Isohyet

and **coldest** continent on Earth

Difficulty level: **Medium**

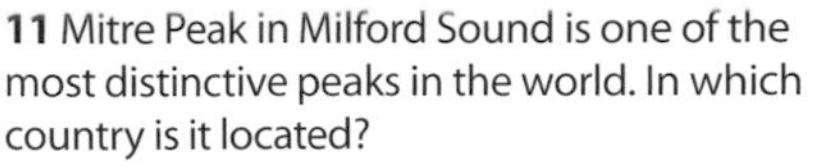

11 Mitre Peak in Milford Sound is one of the most distinctive peaks in the world. In which country is it located?

a New Zealand
b Australia
c Sweden
d Norway

12 Monument Valley is famous for its sandstone rock formations, called mesas and buttes. Where is it?

a US
b Canada
c Mexico
d Brazil

13 Which city in the US is known as the Windy City?

a San Francisco
b Detroit
c New York
d Chicago

14 The largest yucca plants are found in the Mojave Desert. What are they called?

a Datilillos
b Izotes
c Joshua trees
d Texas bayonettes

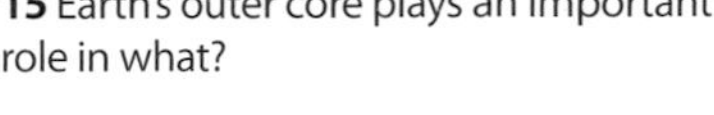

15 Earth's outer core plays an important role in what?

a Magnetic field
b Climate
c Oceans
d Mountains

16 Which of the following plates does not border the Cocos Plate?

a Caribbean
b Pacific
c Philippine
d Nazca

17 The city of Chicago is beside which of the Great Lakes?

a Lake Michigan
b Lake Huron
c Lake Erie
d Lake Superior

18 When organic sediments lithify, what might they form?

a Lignite
b Anthracite
c Coal
d All of these

19 Which of these volcanoes is dormant?

a Mount Fogo
b Mount Fuji
c Mount Etna
d Popocatepetl

20 Which of the following is not a form of chalcedony?

a Agate
b Carnelian
c Bloodstone
d Tiger's eye

About **15 per cent** of the world's river

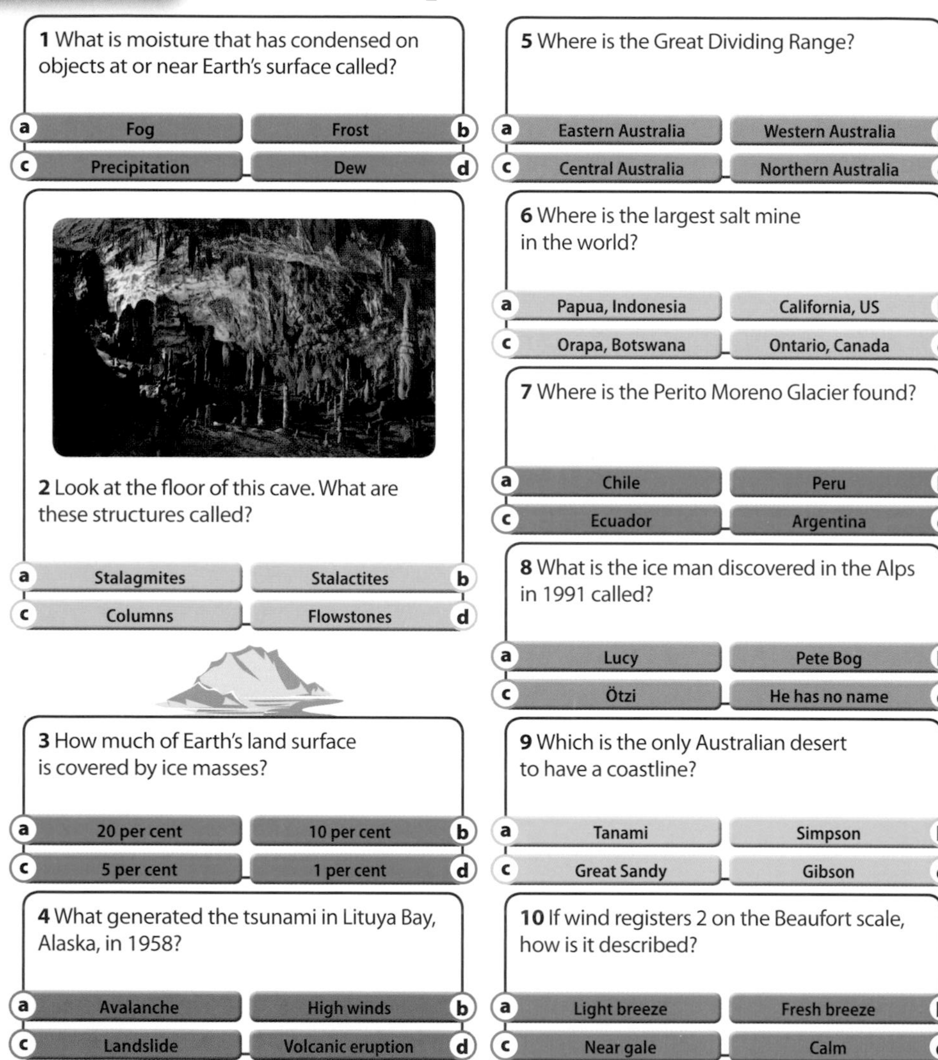

1 What is moisture that has condensed on objects at or near Earth's surface called?

a Fog
b Frost
c Precipitation
d Dew

2 Look at the floor of this cave. What are these structures called?

a Stalagmites
b Stalactites
c Columns
d Flowstones

3 How much of Earth's land surface is covered by ice masses?

a 20 per cent
b 10 per cent
c 5 per cent
d 1 per cent

4 What generated the tsunami in Lituya Bay, Alaska, in 1958?

a Avalanche
b High winds
c Landslide
d Volcanic eruption

5 Where is the Great Dividing Range?

a Eastern Australia
b Western Australia
c Central Australia
d Northern Australia

6 Where is the largest salt mine in the world?

a Papua, Indonesia
b California, US
c Orapa, Botswana
d Ontario, Canada

7 Where is the Perito Moreno Glacier found?

a Chile
b Peru
c Ecuador
d Argentina

8 What is the ice man discovered in the Alps in 1991 called?

a Lucy
b Pete Bog
c Ötzi
d He has no name

9 Which is the only Australian desert to have a coastline?

a Tanami
b Simpson
c Great Sandy
d Gibson

10 If wind registers 2 on the Beaufort scale, how is it described?

a Light breeze
b Fresh breeze
c Near gale
d Calm

water is controlled by **dams**

Difficulty level: **Hard**

11 These hexagonal stone pillars are part of which natural wonder?

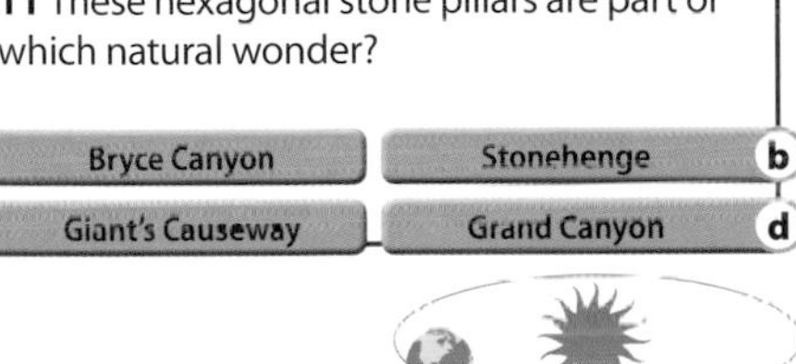

- a Bryce Canyon
- b Stonehenge
- c Giant's Causeway
- d Grand Canyon

12 How far in millions of km (millions of miles) does Earth travel in orbiting the Sun?

- a 150 (93)
- b 200 (125)
- c 50 (31)
- d 25 (15)

13 Approximately how much of the world's fresh surface water is contained in the Great Lakes?

- a 22 per cent
- b 10 per cent
- c 40 per cent
- d 5 per cent

14 What percentage of meteorites are stony meteorites?

- a 56 per cent
- b 36 per cent
- c 86 per cent
- d 16 per cent

15 Why is Mexico City vulnerable if an earthquake occurs?

- a Too many people
- b Ground liquefaction

- c Risk of landslides
- d Risk of flooding

16 How many years ago did the East African Rift first appear?

- a 100 million
- b 100,000
- c 10,000
- d 40 million

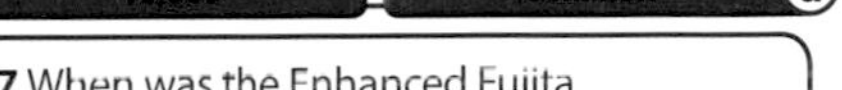

17 When was the Enhanced Fujita scale adopted?

- a 1977
- b 2007
- c 1997
- d 1987

18 Which is the largest man-made lake in the world?

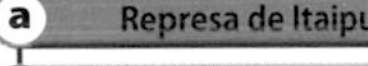

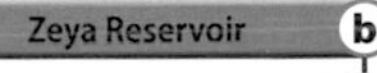

- a Represa de Itaipu
- b Zeya Reservoir
- c Lake Nasser
- d Lake Mead

19 What percentage of the world's plant species are found in tropical rainforests?

- a 11 per cent
- b 66 per cent

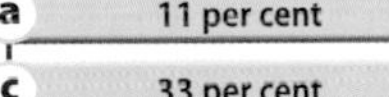

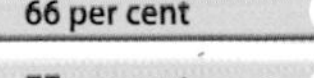

- c 33 per cent
- d 77 per cent

20 According to most geologists, at which height does a hill become a mountain?

- a 1,000m (3,280ft)
- b 305m (1,000ft)
- c 610m (2,000ft)
- d 500m (1,640ft)

Quiz 28

It's not only **Earth** that shakes – there are

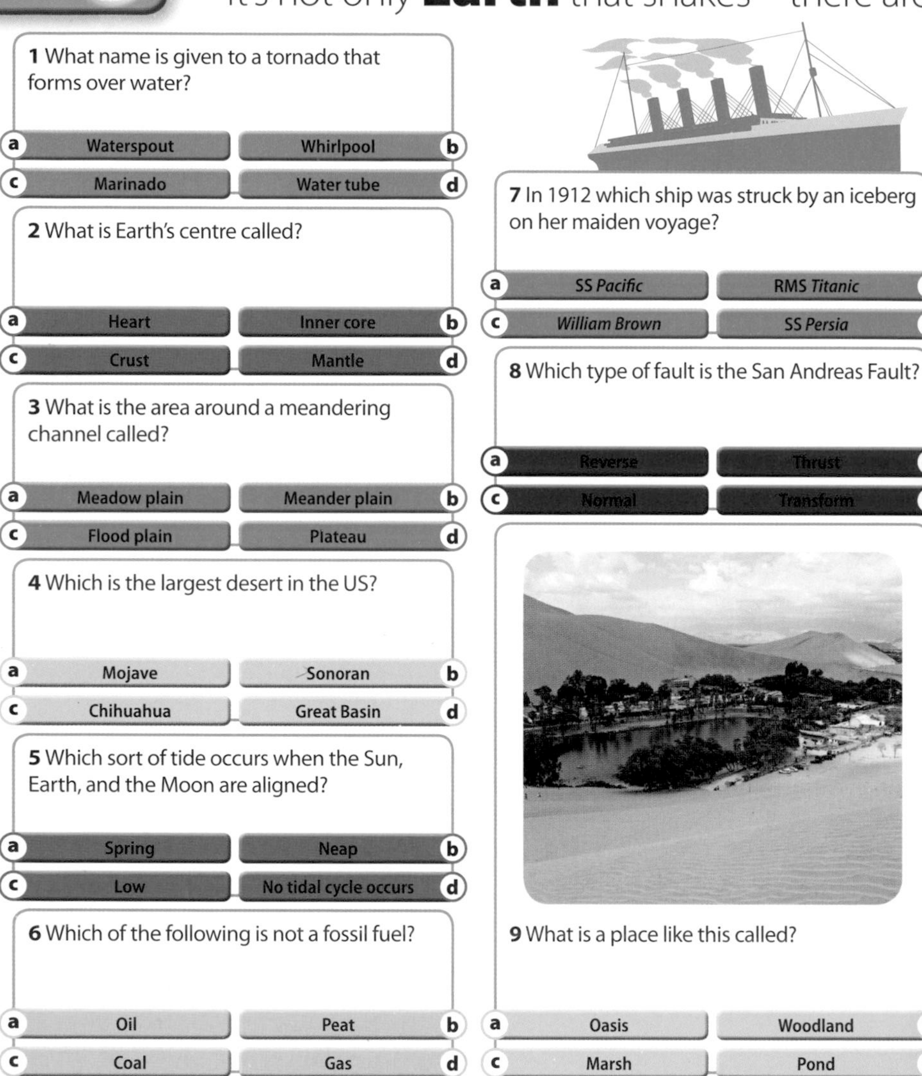

1 What name is given to a tornado that forms over water?

- a Waterspout
- b Whirlpool
- c Marinado
- d Water tube

2 What is Earth's centre called?

- a Heart
- b Inner core
- c Crust
- d Mantle

3 What is the area around a meandering channel called?

- a Meadow plain
- b Meander plain
- c Flood plain
- d Plateau

4 Which is the largest desert in the US?

- a Mojave
- b Sonoran
- c Chihuahua
- d Great Basin

5 Which sort of tide occurs when the Sun, Earth, and the Moon are aligned?

- a Spring
- b Neap
- c Low
- d No tidal cycle occurs

6 Which of the following is not a fossil fuel?

- a Oil
- b Peat
- c Coal
- d Gas

7 In 1912 which ship was struck by an iceberg on her maiden voyage?

- a SS *Pacific*
- b RMS *Titanic*
- c *William Brown*
- d SS *Persia*

8 Which type of fault is the San Andreas Fault?

- a Reverse
- b Thrust
- c Normal
- d Transform

9 What is a place like this called?

- a Oasis
- b Woodland
- c Marsh
- d Pond

10 How many countries suffered casualties in the 2004 Indian Ocean tsunami?

a 7
b 3
c 23
d 14

13 Which of the following can erode rocks?

a Water
b Ice
c Wind
d All of these

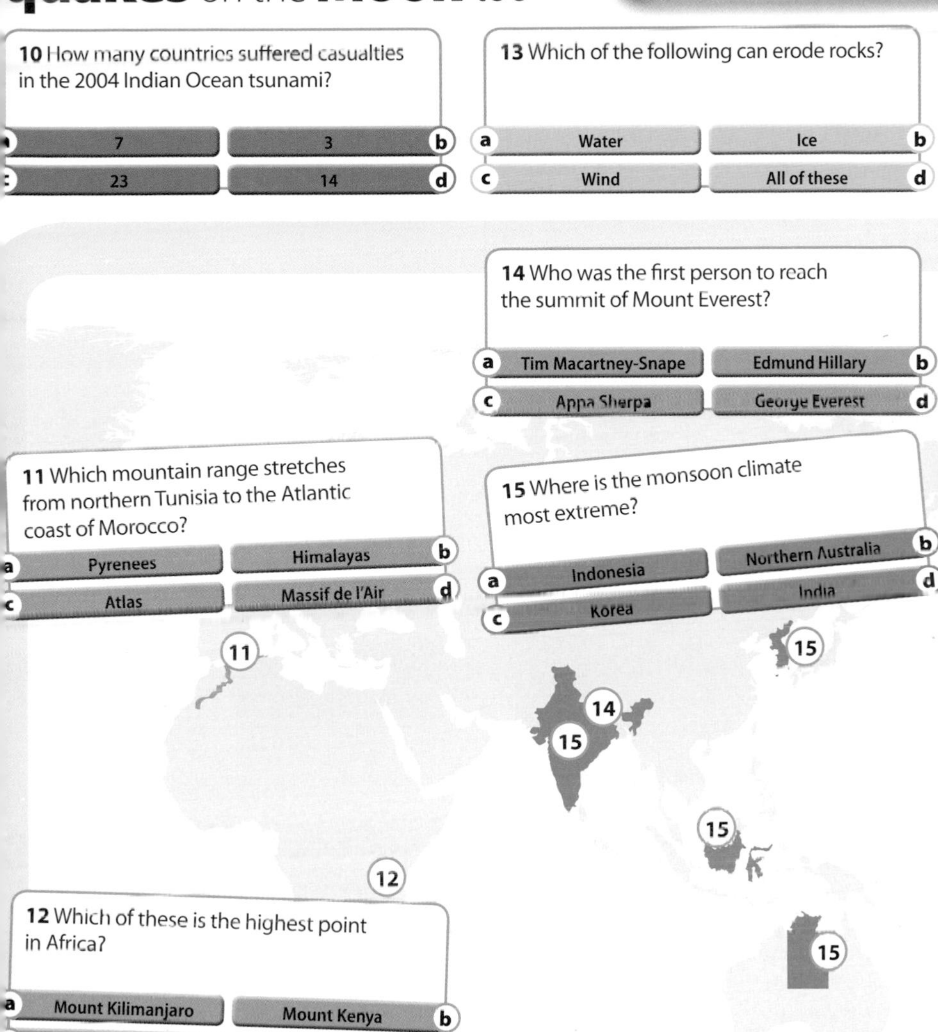

14 Who was the first person to reach the summit of Mount Everest?

a Tim Macartney-Snape
b Edmund Hillary
c Appa Sherpa
d George Everest

11 Which mountain range stretches from northern Tunisia to the Atlantic coast of Morocco?

a Pyrenees
b Himalayas
c Atlas
d Massif de l'Air

15 Where is the monsoon climate most extreme?

a Indonesia
b Northern Australia
c Korea
d India

12 Which of these is the highest point in Africa?

a Mount Kilimanjaro
b Mount Kenya
c The Matterhorn
d Mount Everest

Quiz **29**

Deserts are scorching **hot** by day,

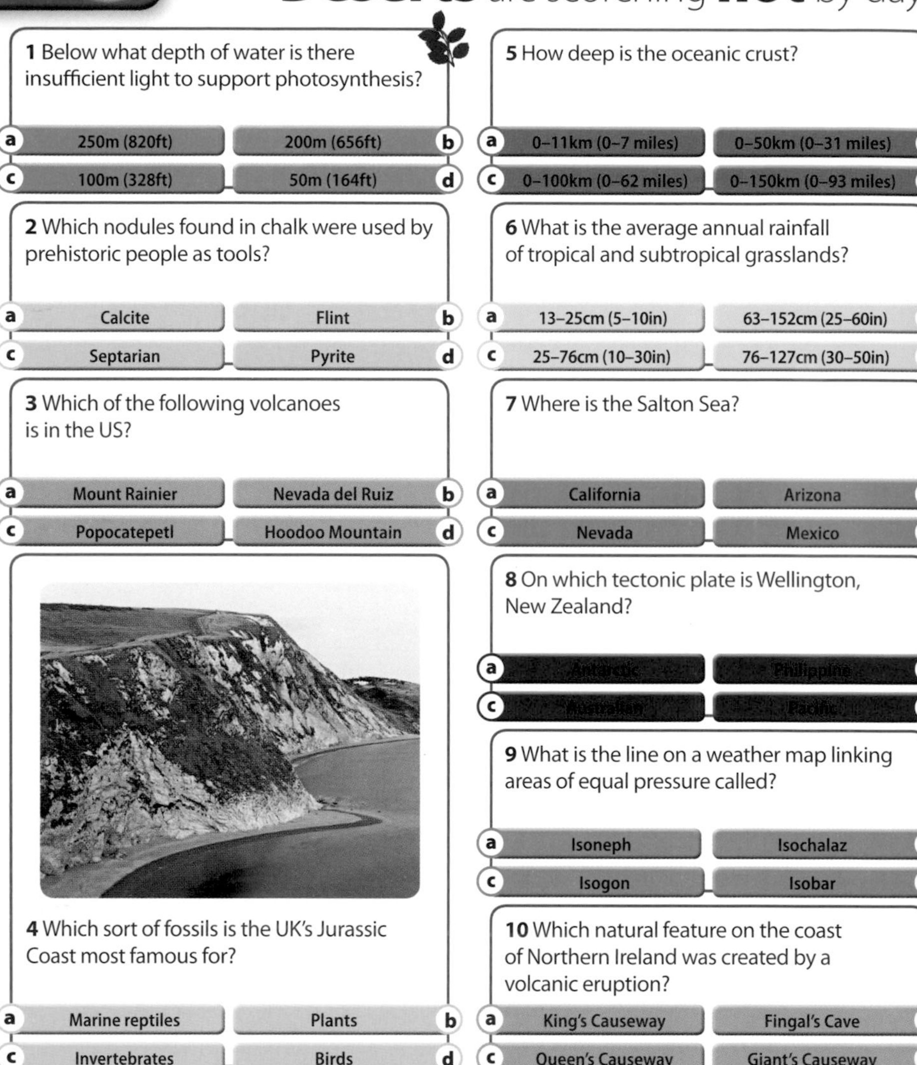

1 Below what depth of water is there insufficient light to support photosynthesis?

- **a** 250m (820ft)
- **b** 200m (656ft)
- **c** 100m (328ft)
- **d** 50m (164ft)

2 Which nodules found in chalk were used by prehistoric people as tools?

- **a** Calcite
- **b** Flint
- **c** Septarian
- **d** Pyrite

3 Which of the following volcanoes is in the US?

- **a** Mount Rainier
- **b** Nevada del Ruiz
- **c** Popocatepetl
- **d** Hoodoo Mountain

4 Which sort of fossils is the UK's Jurassic Coast most famous for?

- **a** Marine reptiles
- **b** Plants
- **c** Invertebrates
- **d** Birds

5 How deep is the oceanic crust?

- **a** 0–11km (0–7 miles)
- **b** 0–50km (0–31 miles)
- **c** 0–100km (0–62 miles)
- **d** 0–150km (0–93 miles)

6 What is the average annual rainfall of tropical and subtropical grasslands?

- **a** 13–25cm (5–10in)
- **b** 63–152cm (25–60in)
- **c** 25–76cm (10–30in)
- **d** 76–127cm (30–50in)

7 Where is the Salton Sea?

- **a** California
- **b** Arizona
- **c** Nevada
- **d** Mexico

8 On which tectonic plate is Wellington, New Zealand?

- **a** Antarctic
- **b** Philippine
- **c** Australian
- **d** Pacific

9 What is the line on a weather map linking areas of equal pressure called?

- **a** Isoneph
- **b** Isochalaz
- **c** Isogon
- **d** Isobar

10 Which natural feature on the coast of Northern Ireland was created by a volcanic eruption?

- **a** King's Causeway
- **b** Fingal's Cave
- **c** Queen's Causeway
- **d** Giant's Causeway

11 The mineral turquoise was particularly important to which ancient culture?

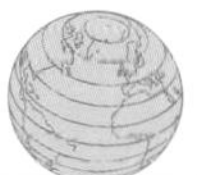

12 How many major circles of latitude are there?

13 In which city is the 1974 film *Earthquake* set?

14 Which lake is a remnant of Lake Bonneville, a great ice-age lake?

15 What is the scientific term for a storm cloud?

a Cumulonimbus
b Stratus
c Cirrus
d Cumulus

16 About how long is the San Andreas Fault zone?

a 3,200km (1,988 miles)
b 1,300km (808 miles)
c 550km (342 miles)
d 50km (31 miles)

17 What is the most common cause of surface waves, giving an ocean motion?

a Rotation of Earth
b Magnetic field
c Air movement
d The Sun and the Moon

18 Which of the other Great Lakes does Lake Huron drain into?

a Lake Ontario
b Lake Superior
c Lake Erie
d Lake Michigan

19 Which process makes the rocks on the bed of a fast-flowing river become smooth over time?

a Corrosion
b Attrition
c Abrasion
d Hydraulic action

20 What is a visible electrical discharge between a cloud and the ground called?

a Lightning flash
b Thunderbolt
c Fork lightning
d Sheet lightning

More than **2,000** species of **fish** have

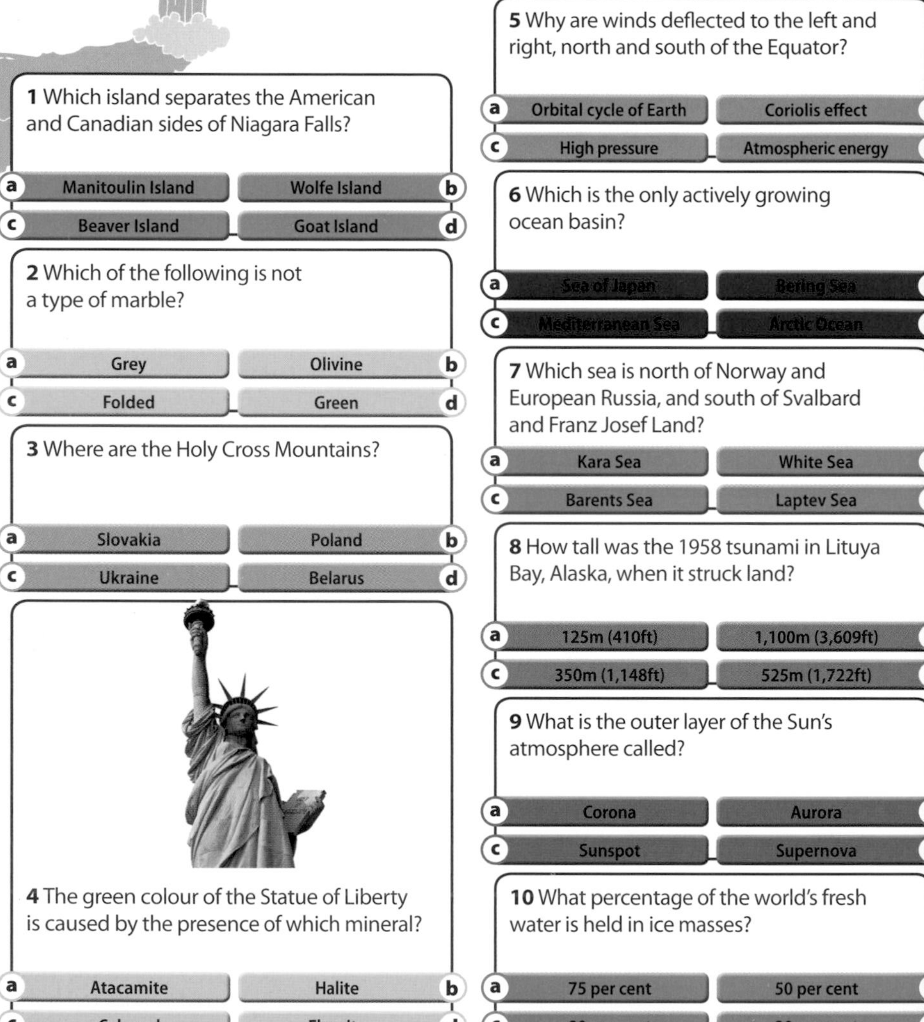

1 Which island separates the American and Canadian sides of Niagara Falls?

a Manitoulin Island
b Wolfe Island
c Beaver Island
d Goat Island

2 Which of the following is not a type of marble?

a Grey
b Olivine
c Folded
d Green

3 Where are the Holy Cross Mountains?

a Slovakia
b Poland
c Ukraine
d Belarus

4 The green colour of the Statue of Liberty is caused by the presence of which mineral?

a Atacamite
b Halite
c Calomel
d Fluorite

5 Why are winds deflected to the left and right, north and south of the Equator?

a Orbital cycle of Earth
b Coriolis effect
c High pressure
d Atmospheric energy

6 Which is the only actively growing ocean basin?

a Sea of Japan
b Bering Sea
c Mediterranean Sea
d Arctic Ocean

7 Which sea is north of Norway and European Russia, and south of Svalbard and Franz Josef Land?

a Kara Sea
b White Sea
c Barents Sea
d Laptev Sea

8 How tall was the 1958 tsunami in Lituya Bay, Alaska, when it struck land?

a 125m (410ft)
b 1,100m (3,609ft)
c 350m (1,148ft)
d 525m (1,722ft)

9 What is the outer layer of the Sun's atmosphere called?

a Corona
b Aurora
c Sunspot
d Supernova

10 What percentage of the world's fresh water is held in ice masses?

a 75 per cent
b 50 per cent
c 90 per cent
d 20 per cent

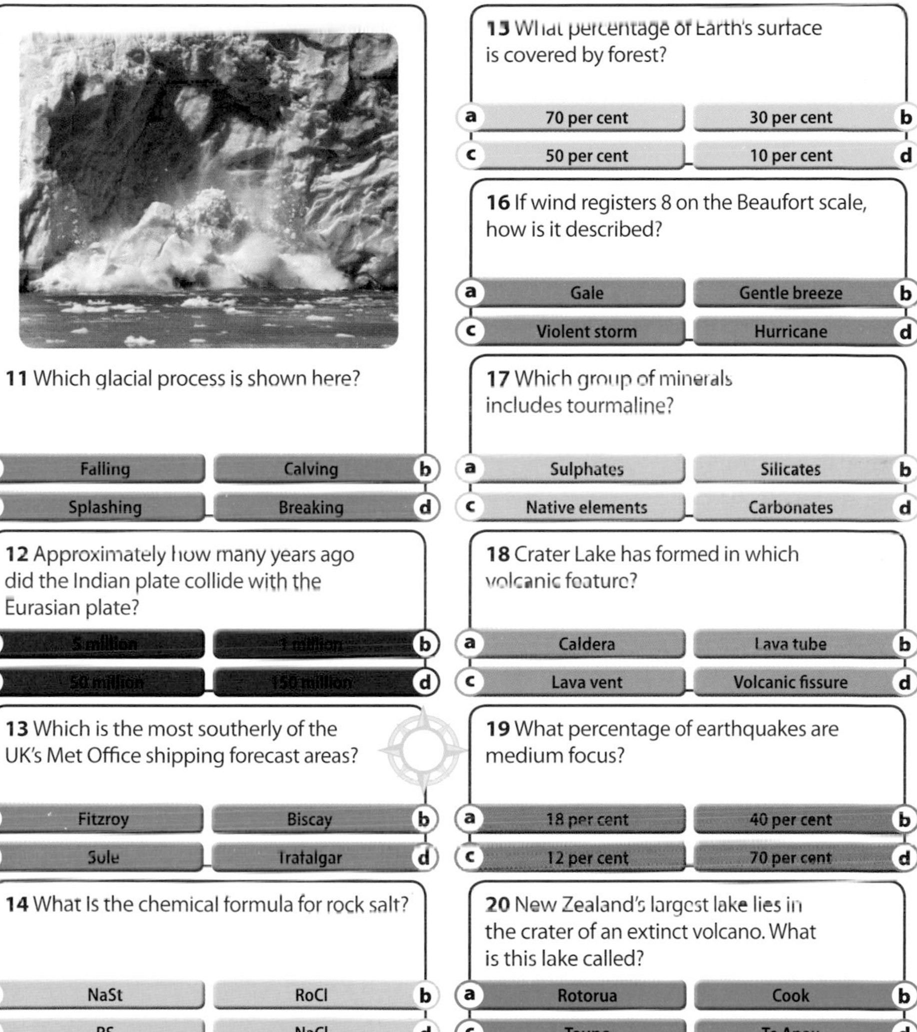

11 Which glacial process is shown here?

a Falling | b Calving
c Splashing | d Breaking

12 Approximately how many years ago did the Indian plate collide with the Eurasian plate?

a 5 million | b 1 million
c 50 million | d 150 million

13 Which is the most southerly of the UK's Met Office shipping forecast areas?

a Fitzroy | b Biscay
c Sole | d Trafalgar

14 What is the chemical formula for rock salt?

a NaSt | b RoCl
c RS | d NaCl

15 What percentage of Earth's surface is covered by forest?

a 70 per cent | b 30 per cent
c 50 per cent | d 10 per cent

16 If wind registers 8 on the Beaufort scale, how is it described?

a Gale | b Gentle breeze
c Violent storm | d Hurricane

17 Which group of minerals includes tourmaline?

a Sulphates | b Silicates
c Native elements | d Carbonates

18 Crater Lake has formed in which volcanic feature?

a Caldera | b Lava tube
c Lava vent | d Volcanic fissure

19 What percentage of earthquakes are medium focus?

a 18 per cent | b 40 per cent
c 12 per cent | d 70 per cent

20 New Zealand's largest lake lies in the crater of an extinct volcano. What is this lake called?

a Rotorua | b Cook
c Taupo | d Te Anau

Quiz **31**

Some Antarctic **valleys** have **not** seen

1 Which monument featured in the 1977 science-fiction film *Close Encounters of the Third Kind*?

a Stonehenge
b Devils Tower
c Sugarloaf Mountain
d Uluru

2 In which desert is Death Valley?

a Mojave
b Sonoran
c Great Basin
d Chihuahua

3 Which term is used to describe whirlwinds of sand that form in deserts?

a Tumbleweeds
b Dust devils
c Sandstorms
d Sandspouts

4 Which animal is known as the "ship of the desert"?

a

b

c

d

5 The name of which natural hazard comes from a Japanese word meaning "harbour wave"?

a Tsunami
b Typhoon
c Tornado
d Monsoon

6 When it is winter in the southern hemisphere, which season is it in the northern hemisphere?

a Spring
b Autumn
c Summer
d Winter

7 Which kind of rock forms mainly from fossils?

a Sandstone
b Shale
c Basalt
d Chalk

rain for **4 million** years

Difficulty level: **Easy**

8 On which tectonic plate is Tokyo, the capital of Japan, situated?

a African
b S American
c Eurasian
d Australian

9 Which river flows through this famous canyon in the US?

a Hudson
b Hoover
c Mississippi
d Colorado

10 Which ocean current improves the climate of the UK?

a Gulf Stream
b North Equatorial Current
c Canary Current
d North Atlantic Drift

11 Rocks that form from either magma or lava are known as…

a Sedimentary
b Continental
c Igneous
d Metamorphic

12 Which is the only liquid layer of Earth?

a Inner core
b Outer core
c Outer mantle
d Oceanic crust

13 Which is the only US state not on the N American plate?

a Alaska
b Florida
c Oregon
d Hawaii

14 What is the solid material carried by a river called?

a Turbulence
b Water
c Sediment load
d Boulders

15 What is the chemical symbol of Iron?

a In
b F
c Fe
d Ir

Quiz 32

Europe may be named after the

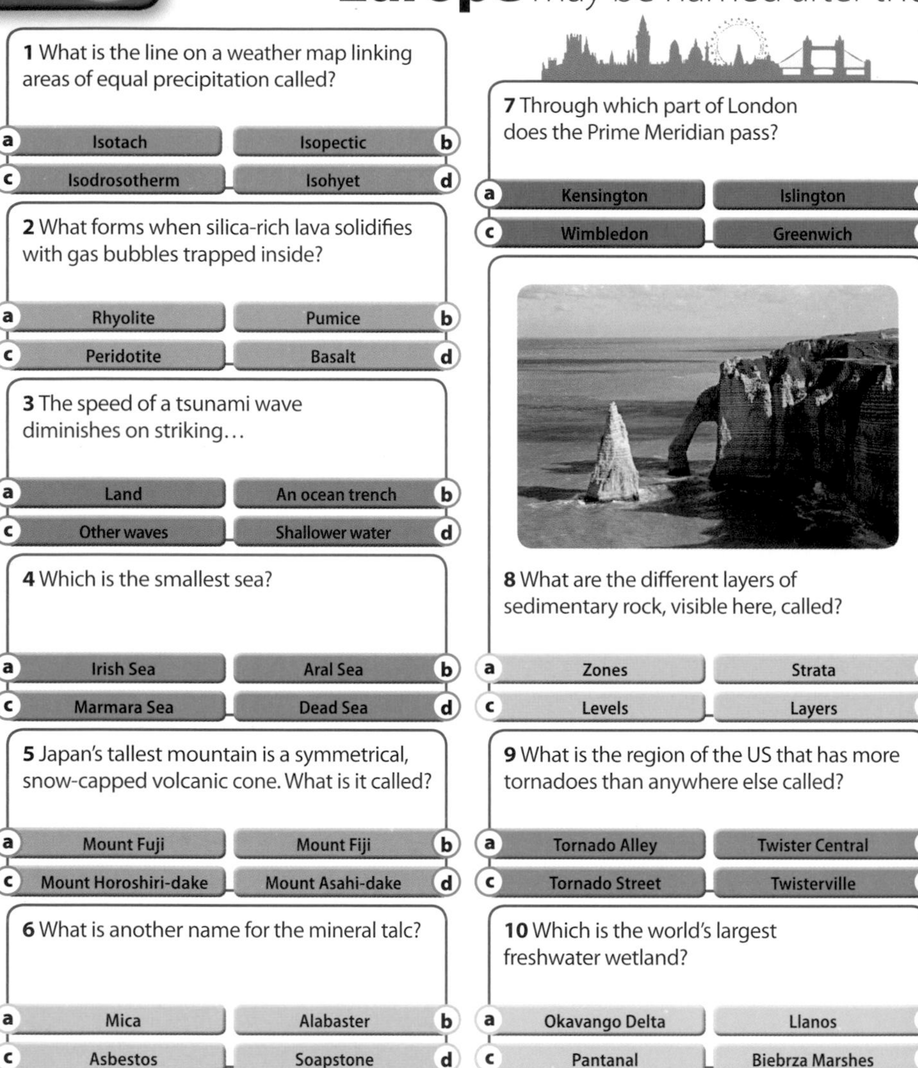

1 What is the line on a weather map linking areas of equal precipitation called?

a Isotach
b Isopectic
c Isodrosotherm
d Isohyet

2 What forms when silica-rich lava solidifies with gas bubbles trapped inside?

a Rhyolite
b Pumice
c Peridotite
d Basalt

3 The speed of a tsunami wave diminishes on striking…

a Land
b An ocean trench
c Other waves
d Shallower water

4 Which is the smallest sea?

a Irish Sea
b Aral Sea
c Marmara Sea
d Dead Sea

5 Japan's tallest mountain is a symmetrical, snow-capped volcanic cone. What is it called?

a Mount Fuji
b Mount Fiji
c Mount Horoshiri-dake
d Mount Asahi-dake

6 What is another name for the mineral talc?

a Mica
b Alabaster
c Asbestos
d Soapstone

7 Through which part of London does the Prime Meridian pass?

a Kensington
b Islington
c Wimbledon
d Greenwich

8 What are the different layers of sedimentary rock, visible here, called?

a Zones
b Strata
c Levels
d Layers

9 What is the region of the US that has more tornadoes than anywhere else called?

a Tornado Alley
b Twister Central
c Tornado Street
d Twisterville

10 Which is the world's largest freshwater wetland?

a Okavango Delta
b Llanos
c Pantanal
d Biebrza Marshes

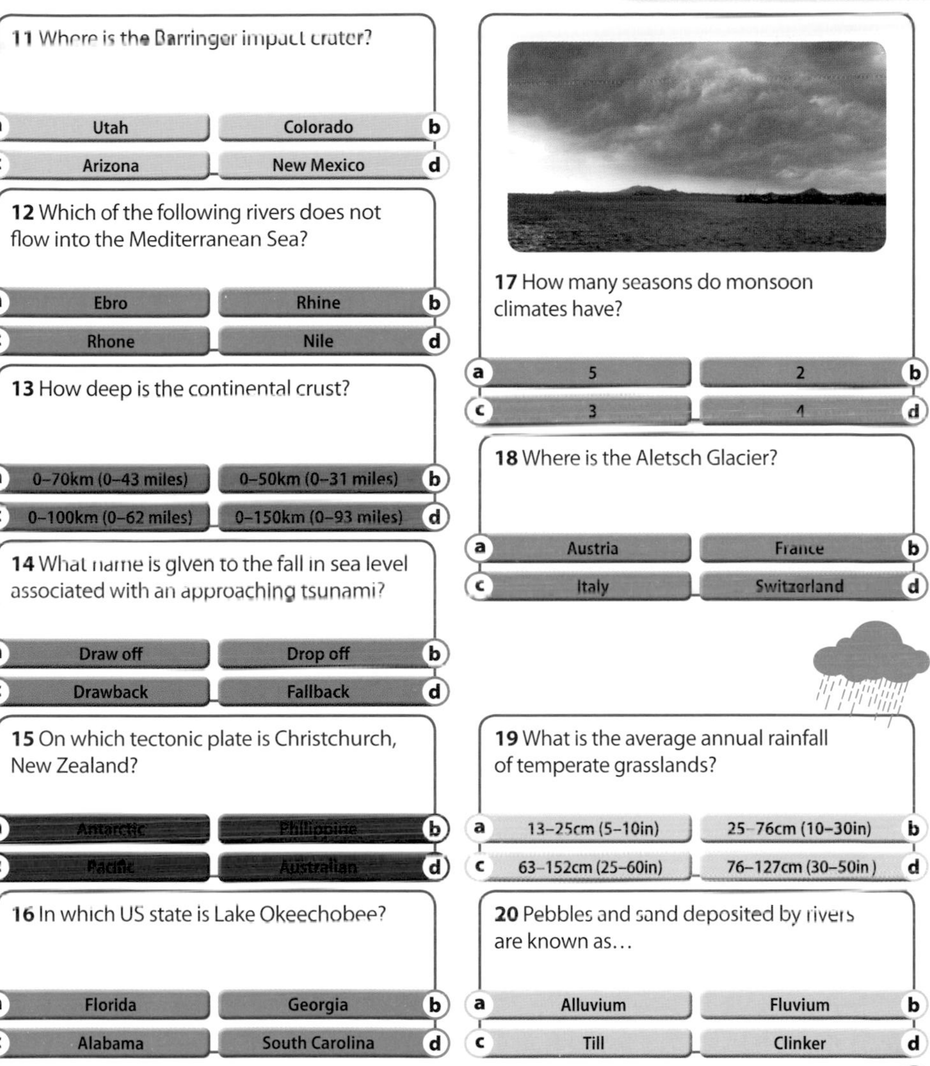

11 Where is the Barringer impact crater?

- a Utah
- b Colorado
- c Arizona
- d New Mexico

12 Which of the following rivers does not flow into the Mediterranean Sea?

- a Ebro
- b Rhine
- c Rhone
- d Nile

13 How deep is the continental crust?

- a 0–70km (0–43 miles)
- b 0–50km (0–31 miles)
- c 0–100km (0–62 miles)
- d 0–150km (0–93 miles)

14 What name is given to the fall in sea level associated with an approaching tsunami?

- a Draw off
- b Drop off
- c Drawback
- d Fallback

15 On which tectonic plate is Christchurch, New Zealand?

- a Antarctic
- b Philippine
- c Pacific
- d Australian

16 In which US state is Lake Okeechobee?

- a Florida
- b Georgia
- c Alabama
- d South Carolina

17 How many seasons do monsoon climates have?

- a 5
- b 2
- c 3
- d 4

18 Where is the Aletsch Glacier?

- a Austria
- b France
- c Italy
- d Switzerland

19 What is the average annual rainfall of temperate grasslands?

- a 13–25cm (5–10in)
- b 25–76cm (10–30in)
- c 63–152cm (25–60in)
- d 76–127cm (30–50in)

20 Pebbles and sand deposited by rivers are known as…

- a Alluvium
- b Fluvium
- c Till
- d Clinker

Quiz 33

The **Assyrians** called **Asia**

1 Which country currently emits most greenhouse gases?

a US
b Russia
c UK
d China

2 The Mediterranean evergreen forests are an important source of cork. How often can it be harvested?

a Every 15 years
b Every year
c Every 9 years
d Every 4 years

3 Who was the first person to survive going over Niagara Falls in a barrel?

a Annie Taylor
b Bobby Leach
c Charles Stephens
d Nathan Boya

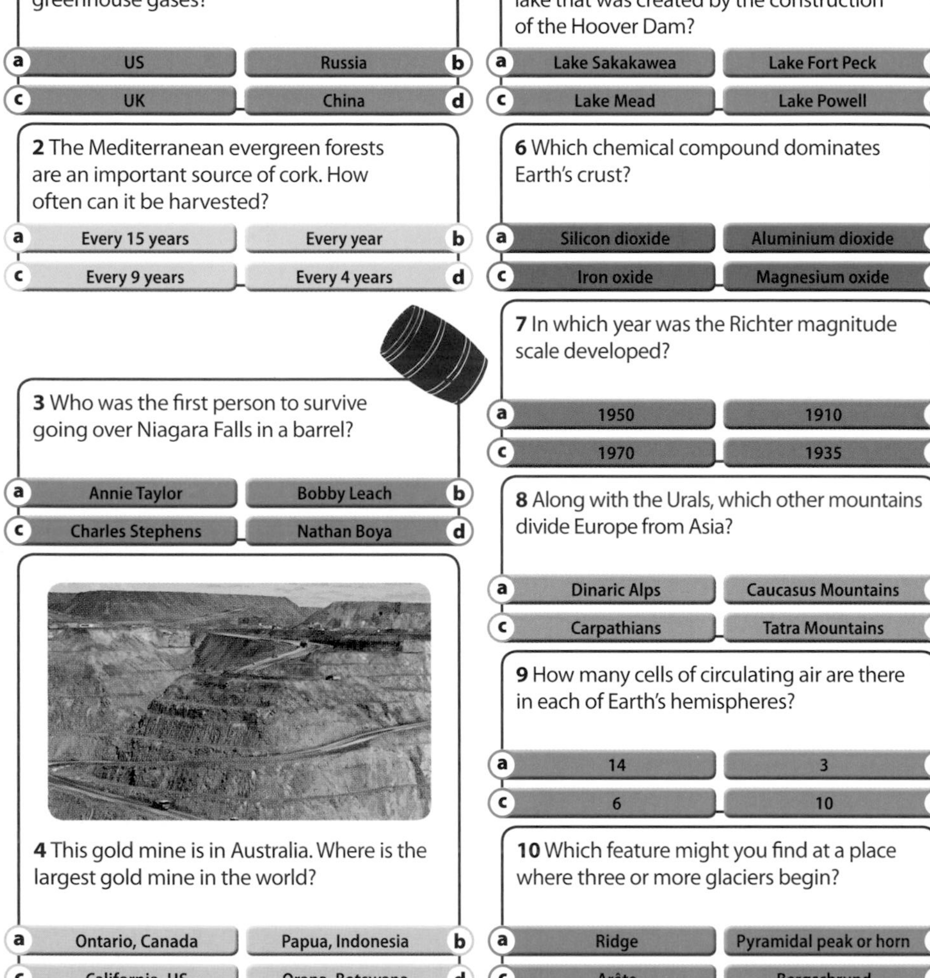

4 This gold mine is in Australia. Where is the largest gold mine in the world?

a Ontario, Canada
b Papua, Indonesia
c California, US
d Orapa, Botswana

5 What is the name of the man-made lake that was created by the construction of the Hoover Dam?

a Lake Sakakawea
b Lake Fort Peck
c Lake Mead
d Lake Powell

6 Which chemical compound dominates Earth's crust?

a Silicon dioxide
b Aluminium dioxide
c Iron oxide
d Magnesium oxide

7 In which year was the Richter magnitude scale developed?

a 1950
b 1910
c 1970
d 1935

8 Along with the Urals, which other mountains divide Europe from Asia?

a Dinaric Alps
b Caucasus Mountains
c Carpathians
d Tatra Mountains

9 How many cells of circulating air are there in each of Earth's hemispheres?

a 14
b 3
c 6
d 10

10 Which feature might you find at a place where three or more glaciers begin?

a Ridge
b Pyramidal peak or horn
c Arête
d Bergschrund

"the **land** of the **sunrise**"

Difficulty level: **Hard**

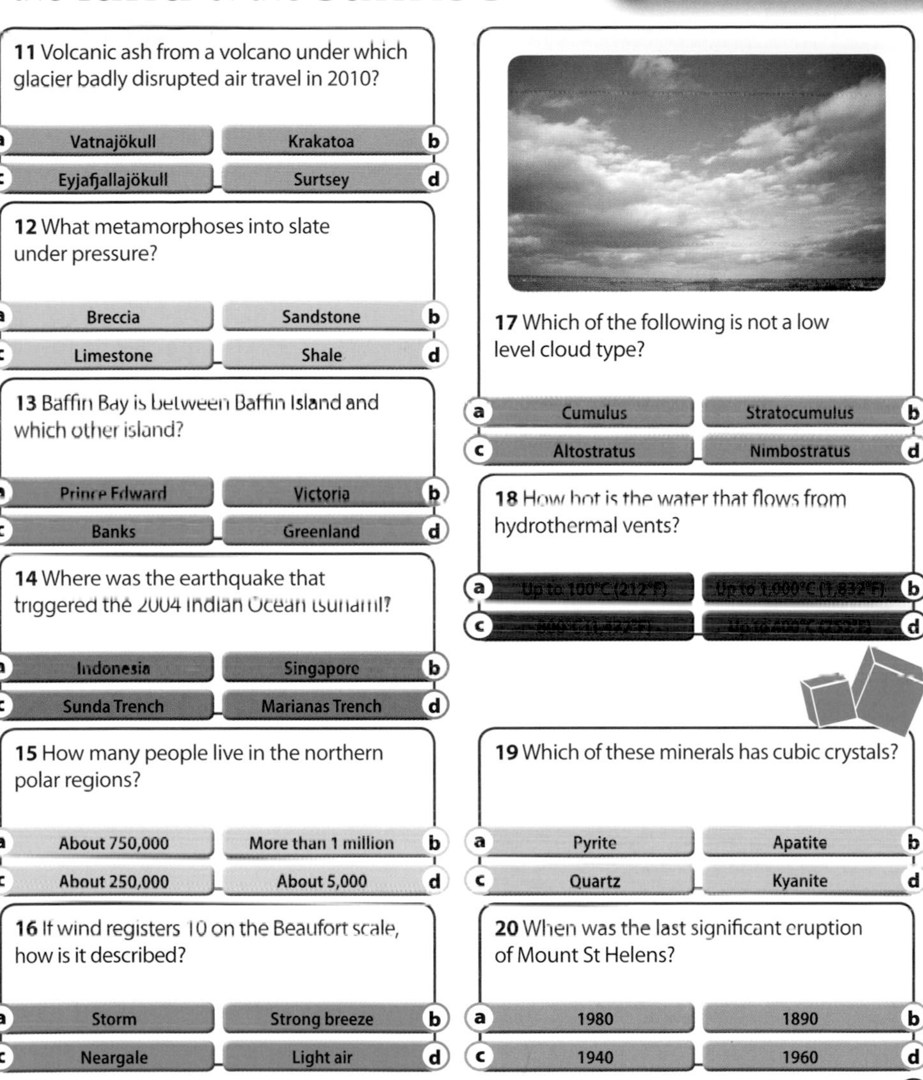

11 Volcanic ash from a volcano under which glacier badly disrupted air travel in 2010?

- a Vatnajökull
- b Krakatoa
- c Eyjafjallajökull
- d Surtsey

12 What metamorphoses into slate under pressure?

- a Breccia
- b Sandstone
- c Limestone
- d Shale

13 Baffin Bay is between Baffin Island and which other island?

- a Prince Edward
- b Victoria
- c Banks
- d Greenland

14 Where was the earthquake that triggered the 2004 Indian Ocean tsunami?

- a Indonesia
- b Singapore
- c Sunda Trench
- d Marianas Trench

15 How many people live in the northern polar regions?

- a About 750,000
- b More than 1 million
- c About 250,000
- d About 5,000

16 If wind registers 10 on the Beaufort scale, how is it described?

- a Storm
- b Strong breeze
- c Neargale
- d Light air

17 Which of the following is not a low level cloud type?

- a Cumulus
- b Stratocumulus
- c Altostratus
- d Nimbostratus

18 How hot is the water that flows from hydrothermal vents?

- a Up to 100°C (212°F)
- b Up to 1,000°C (1,832°F)
- c 800°C (1,472°F)
- d Up to 400°C (752°F)

19 Which of these minerals has cubic crystals?

- a Pyrite
- b Apatite
- c Quartz
- d Kyanite

20 When was the last significant eruption of Mount St Helens?

- a 1980
- b 1890
- c 1940
- d 1960

Quiz **34**

All **snowflakes** have **six sides**,

1 Woodland soils are generally rich in…

- **a** Water
- **b** Organic matter
- **c** Iron oxide
- **d** Salts

2 Which Italian city was destroyed by Vesuvius in 79CE?

- **a** Pompeii
- **b** Rome
- **c** Milan
- **d** Turin

3 Which term do meteorologists use to describe a heavy snowstorm?

- **a** Hurricane
- **b** El Niño
- **c** Blizzard
- **d** Ice storm

4 Buildings that include which material in their structure are most likely to survive an earthquake?

- **a** Concrete
- **b** Steel
- **c** Wood
- **d** Brick

5 Which musical featured the song "Climb Every Mountain"?

- **a** *Carousel*
- **b** *State Fair*
- **c** *The Sound of Music*
- **d** *South Pacific*

6 Which sea is immediately north of S America and east of Central America?

- **a** Coral
- **b** Banda
- **c** Caribbean
- **d** Sargasso

7 The decline in sea ice is making which animal vulnerable to extinction?

- **a** Polar bear
- **b** Brown bear
- **c** Crab-eater seal
- **d** Killer whale

but **each** one is **unique**

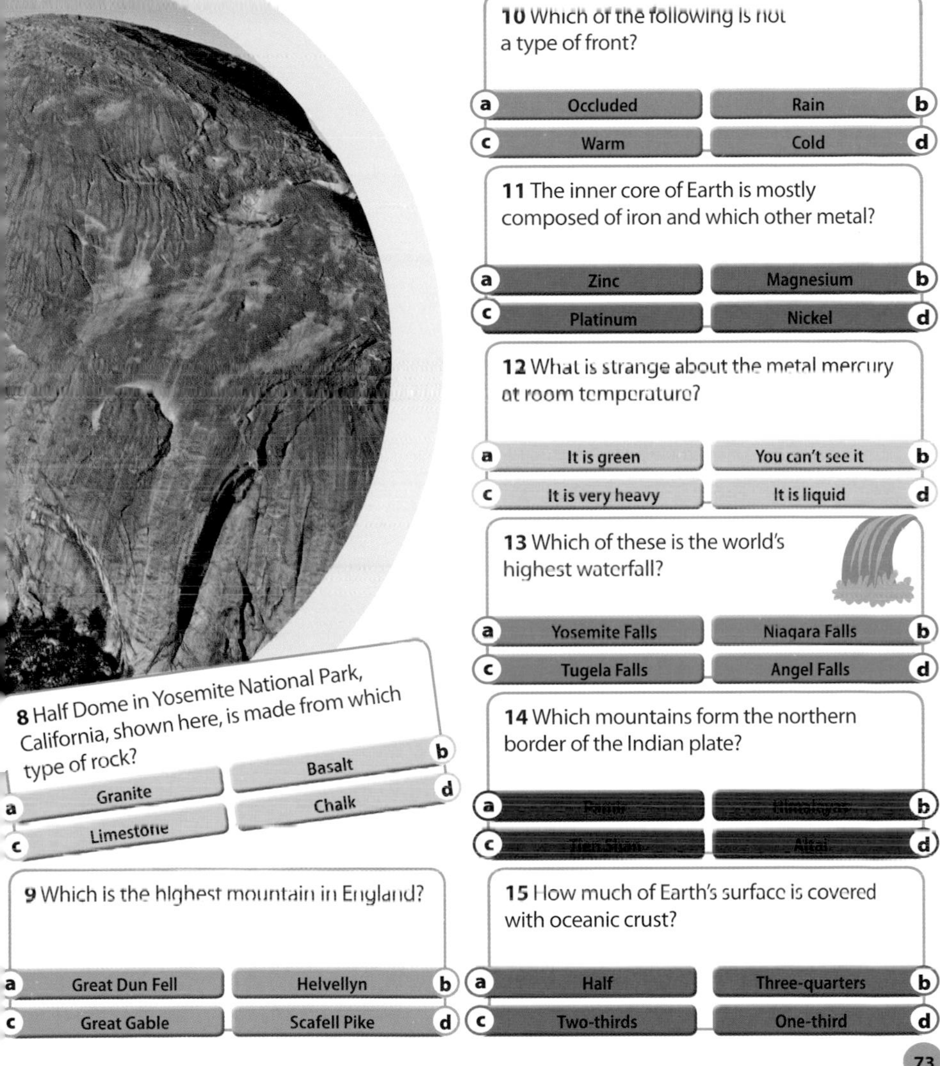

8 Half Dome in Yosemite National Park, California, shown here, is made from which type of rock?

a Granite
b Basalt
c Limestone
d Chalk

9 Which is the highest mountain in England?

a Great Dun Fell
b Helvellyn
c Great Gable
d Scafell Pike

10 Which of the following is not a type of front?

a Occluded
b Rain
c Warm
d Cold

11 The inner core of Earth is mostly composed of iron and which other metal?

a Zinc
b Magnesium
c Platinum
d Nickel

12 What is strange about the metal mercury at room temperature?

a It is green
b You can't see it
c It is very heavy
d It is liquid

13 Which of these is the world's highest waterfall?

a Yosemite Falls
b Niagara Falls
c Tugela Falls
d Angel Falls

14 Which mountains form the northern border of the Indian plate?

a Pamir
b Himalayas
c Tien Shan
d Altai

15 How much of Earth's surface is covered with oceanic crust?

a Half
b Three-quarters
c Two-thirds
d One-third

Quiz 35

90 per cent of Earth's volcanoes lie

1 In the last 50 years of the 20th century, which US state suffered most from tornadoes?

a Kansas
b Missouri
c Georgia
d Texas

2 This is a rocky shore at high tide. The gravitational force that causes tides is known as what?

a Tractive
b Magnetic
c Electrostatic
d Repulsive

3 What was the emerald in the 1984 film *Romancing the Stone* called?

a El Corazon
b El Diablo
c Sankara
d Pink Panther

4 What forms when a loop of river gets cut off from the main flow?

a Oxbow lake
b Meander pool
c J-pond
d Swamp

5 Where is the deepest part of the world's oceans?

a Kuril Trench
b Philippine Trench
c Marianas Trench
d Japan Trench

6 What, with an average depth of just 7m (23ft), is the world's shallowest sea?

a Sea of Okhotsk
b Sea of Azov
c Baltic Sea
d Irish Sea

7 Pyroclastic material thrown out by a volcano is called what?

a Moraine
b Tephra
c Scree
d Talus

8 In which wetland are about 90 per cent of the world's scarlet ibises found?

a Okavango Delta
b Llanos
c Everglades
d Carmargue

9 The source of the Hudson River is in which mountain range?

a Appalachians
b Black Hills
c Blue Ridge Mountains
d Adirondacks

10 About how many "minor" tectonic plates are there?

a 12
b 18
c 5
d 28

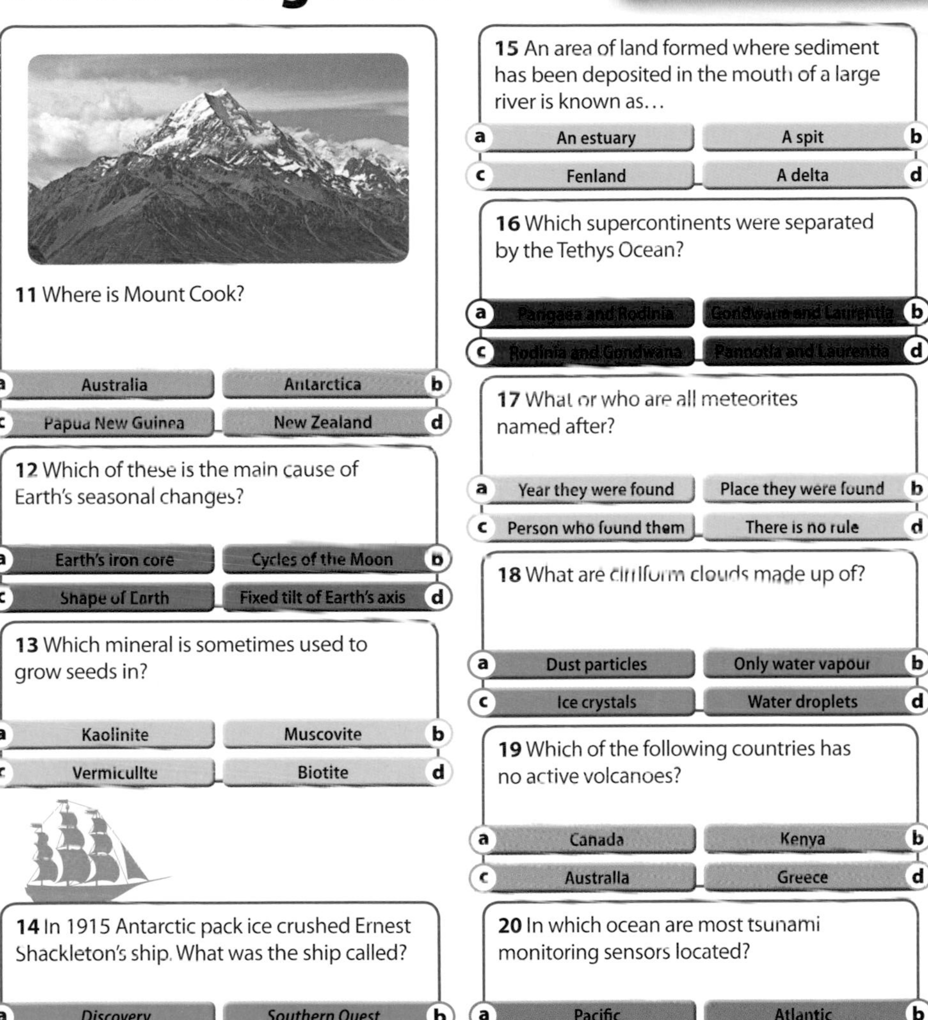

11 Where is Mount Cook?

- a Australia
- b Antarctica
- c Papua New Guinea
- d New Zealand

12 Which of these is the main cause of Earth's seasonal changes?

- a Earth's iron core
- b Cycles of the Moon
- c Shape of Earth
- d Fixed tilt of Earth's axis

13 Which mineral is sometimes used to grow seeds in?

- a Kaolinite
- b Muscovite
- c Vermiculite
- d Biotite

14 In 1915 Antarctic pack ice crushed Ernest Shackleton's ship. What was the ship called?

- a *Discovery*
- b *Southern Quest*
- c *Endurance*
- d *Endeavour*

15 An area of land formed where sediment has been deposited in the mouth of a large river is known as…

- a An estuary
- b A spit
- c Fenland
- d A delta

16 Which supercontinents were separated by the Tethys Ocean?

- a Pangaea and Rodinia
- b Gondwana and Laurentia
- c Rodinia and Gondwana
- d Pannotia and Laurentia

17 What or who are all meteorites named after?

- a Year they were found
- b Place they were found
- c Person who found them
- d There is no rule

18 What are cirriform clouds made up of?

- a Dust particles
- b Only water vapour
- c Ice crystals
- d Water droplets

19 Which of the following countries has no active volcanoes?

- a Canada
- b Kenya
- c Australia
- d Greece

20 In which ocean are most tsunami monitoring sensors located?

- a Pacific
- b Atlantic
- c Indian
- d Southern

In 1943 a Mexican **farmer** discovered the

1 On which continents do you find hot climates with seasonal, non-monsoonal rain?

a Africa and Asia
b S and C America, Asia
c S and C America, Africa
d All continents

2 Rubies and sapphires are the same mineral. Which is it?

a Spinel
b Chrysoberyl
c Rutile
d Corundum

3 In which country is K2?

a India
b Pakistan
c Bhutan
d Tibet

4 Which of the following would you not find in Antarctica?

a Dry valleys
b Forests
c Volcanoes
d Nunataks

5 How often does a proxigean spring tide occur?

a Every 1.5 years
b Every 5 years
c Every 10 years
d Every 3 years

6 The River Volga starts in which upland marshy region?

a Upper Dvuobje
b Valdai Hills
c Pripet Marshes
d Kama-Bakaldino Mires

7 What causes the darkening of the water emitted from black smokers?

a Precipitation of calcium
b Micro-organisms
c Precipitation of sulphides
d All of these

8 What is the name for a giant boulder dumped by a glacier far from its site of origin?

a Erratic
b Stone
c Esker
d Drumlin

9 What is the upper limit on the Richter scale?

a 10
b 100
c 50
d No upper limit

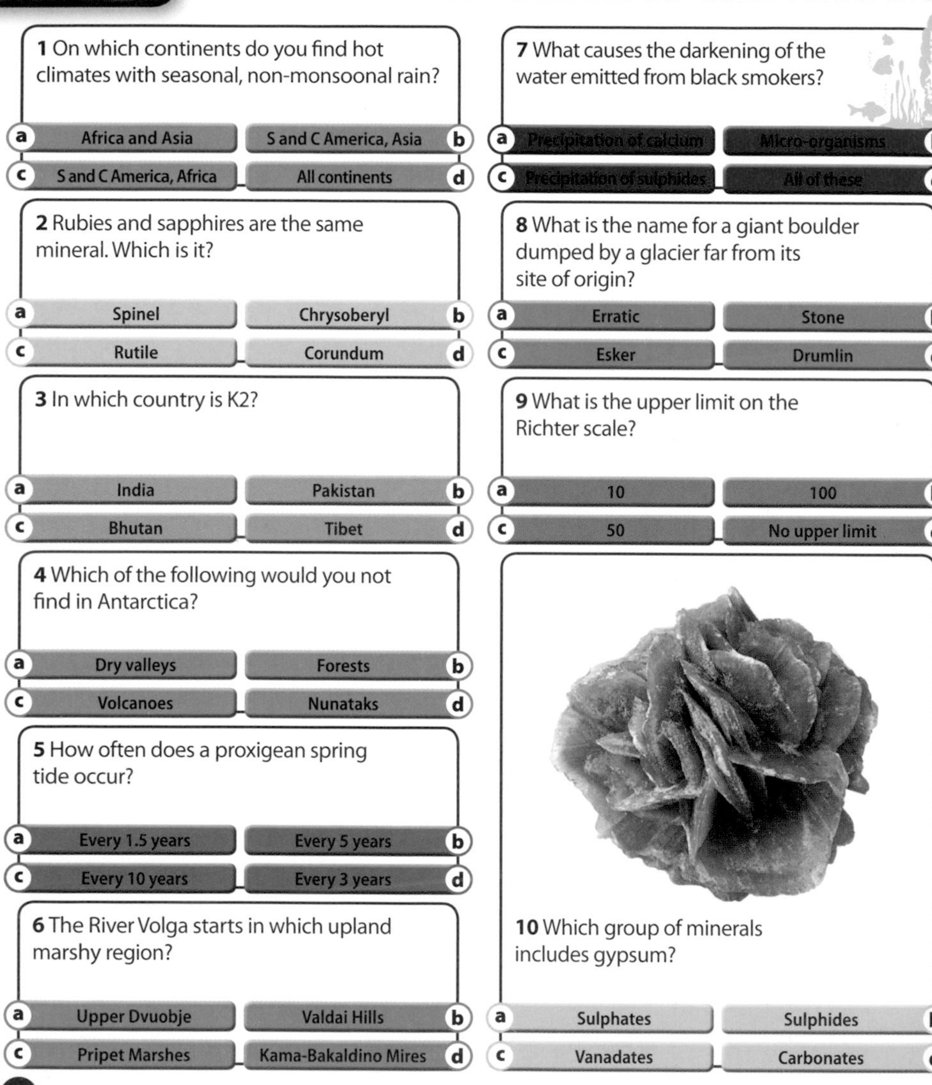

10 Which group of minerals includes gypsum?

a Sulphates
b Sulphides
c Vanadates
d Carbonates

Paricutin **volcano** in a **field**

Difficulty level: **Hard**

11 Which type of cloud are warm fronts normally associated with?

12 Under metamorphism, slate changes into other rocks. Which of these would it not turn into?

a Schist
b Gneiss
c Hornfels
d Phyllite

13 Which type of delta has formed at the mouth of the Mississippi?

a Lacustrine
b Fan (arcuate)
c Cuspate
d Bird's foot

14 About how many species of eucalyptus are there?

15 Which silicate has the chemical composition SiO_2?

16 Which bay lies between the Canadian provinces of Nova Scotia and New Brunswick?

17 For how many years has the Pacific plate been grinding against the N American plate?

18 Which is the highest active volcano on Earth?

a Cotopaxi
b Masaya
c El Chichón
d Arenal

19 What percentage of earthquakes are deep focus?

20 If wind registers 12 on the Beaufort scale, how is it described?

a Storm
b Gale
c Hurricane
d Moderate breeze

Quiz 37

Three-quarters of Earth's naturally

1 When it snows, hails, sleets, or rains, which process is occurring?

a Precipitation
b Condensation
c Evaporation
d Glaciation

2 At what height is standard atmospheric pressure defined?

a 3m (10ft)
b 305m (1,001ft)
c Sea level
d 30m (98ft)

3 What is the name of the zone of volcanic activity around the Pacific Ocean?

a Pacific Band of Ash
b Pacific Ring of Fire
c Pacific Ring of Ash
d Pacific Band of Fire

4 Which of the following weather hazards is not linked to tornadoes?

a Lightning
b Hailstones
c Strong winds
d Storm surge

5 The Universe formed rapidly after an explosion called what?

a Big Bang
b Mega-bang
c Giga-bang
d Atomic Bang

6 What was the length of the biggest known free-hanging stalactite found in Mexico?

a 30m (98ft)
b 5m (16ft)
c 12m (39ft)
d 2m (7ft)

7 What extreme marine environments are found close to mid-oceanic ridges?

a Ocean trenches
b Very deep sediments
c Hydrothermal vents
d Salines

8 The Skeleton Coast is found in which desert?

a Kalahari
b Karoo
c Sahara
d Namib

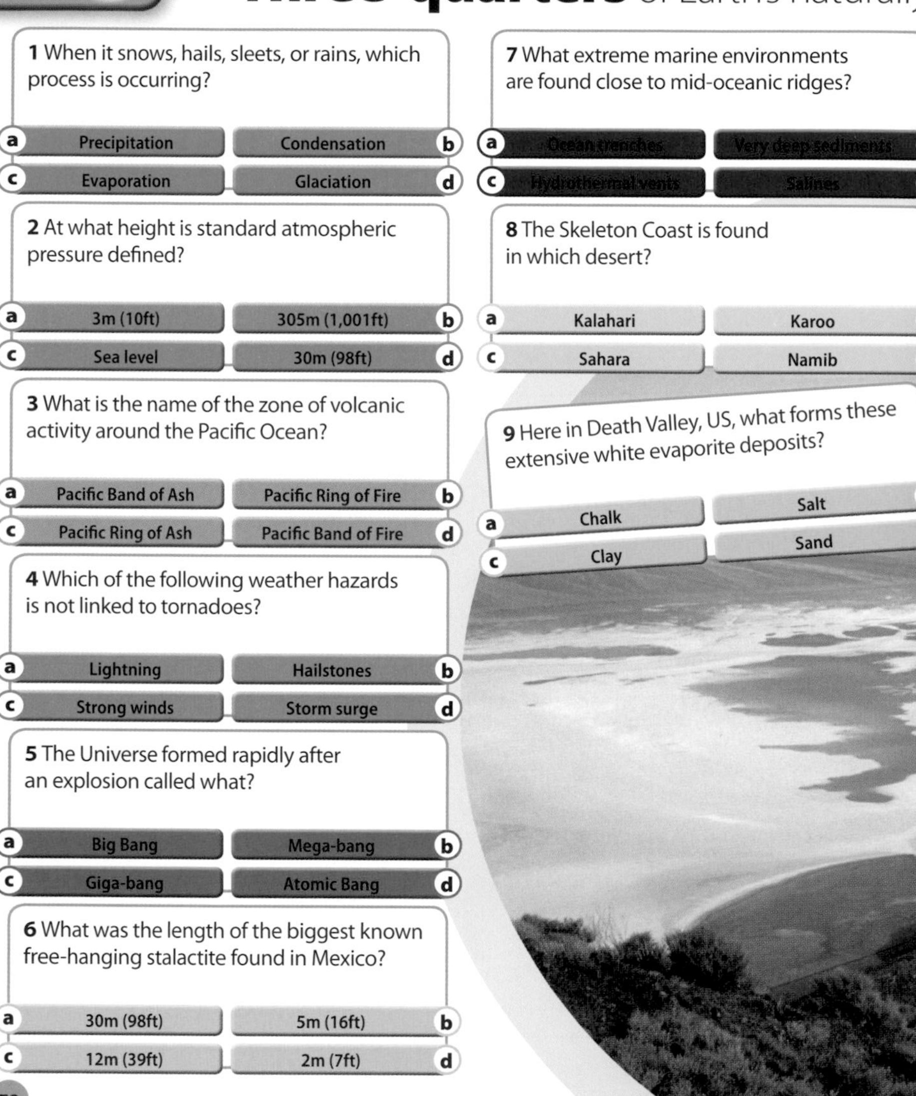

9 Here in Death Valley, US, what forms these extensive white evaporite deposits?

a Chalk
b Salt
c Clay
d Sand

10 Which scientific scale is most commonly used to measure earthquakes?

Mercalli
b Fujita
Saffir–Simpson
d Richter

11 Most of Earth's water is in the oceans and therefore salty. About how much is fresh and not salty?

33 per cent
b 3 per cent
10 per cent
d 25 per cent

12 Where is the continental crust the thickest?

a Under flood plains
b Under cities
c Under hills
d Under young mountains

13 Which biome has the most diverse animal and plant communities?

a Desert
b Grassland
c Forest
d Tundra

14 What colour is lapis lazuli?

a Blue
b Black
c Red
d Green

15 What is the name of the volcano that destroyed Pompeii?

a Mount Vesuvius
b Mount Etna
c Mount Stromboli
d Lipari

Quiz **38**

It is impossible to **predict** an

1 Which sea is 423m (1,388ft) below sea level?

- **a** Red Sea
- **b** Caspian Sea
- **c** Dead Sea
- **d** North Sea

2 In which 1972 film was an ocean liner capsized by a tidal wave?

- **a** *Titanic*
- **b** *The Perfect Storm*
- **c** *Meteor*
- **d** *Poseidon Adventure*

3 What mineral name is given to common rock salt?

- **a** Cryolite
- **b** Carnallite
- **c** Halite
- **d** Fluorite

4 Which dam is the site of the world's largest hydroelectric power facility?

- **a** Hirakud
- **b** Itaipu
- **c** Hoover
- **d** Kariba

5 What does a seismologist study?

- **a** Fossils
- **b** Earthquakes
- **c** Volcanoes
- **d** Weather

6 What do you call a tornado before it touches the ground?

- **a** Tower cloud
- **b** Pre-tornado cloud
- **c** Funnel cloud
- **d** Cumulonimbus cloud

7 How far does Earth's axis tilt from vertical?

- **a** 23.5°
- **b** 40°
- **c** 10.5°
- **d** 60°

8 A film about storm chasers was released in 1996. What was it called?

- **a** *Twister*
- **b** *Storm Cell*
- **c** *The Day After Tomorrow*
- **d** *Tornado Terror*

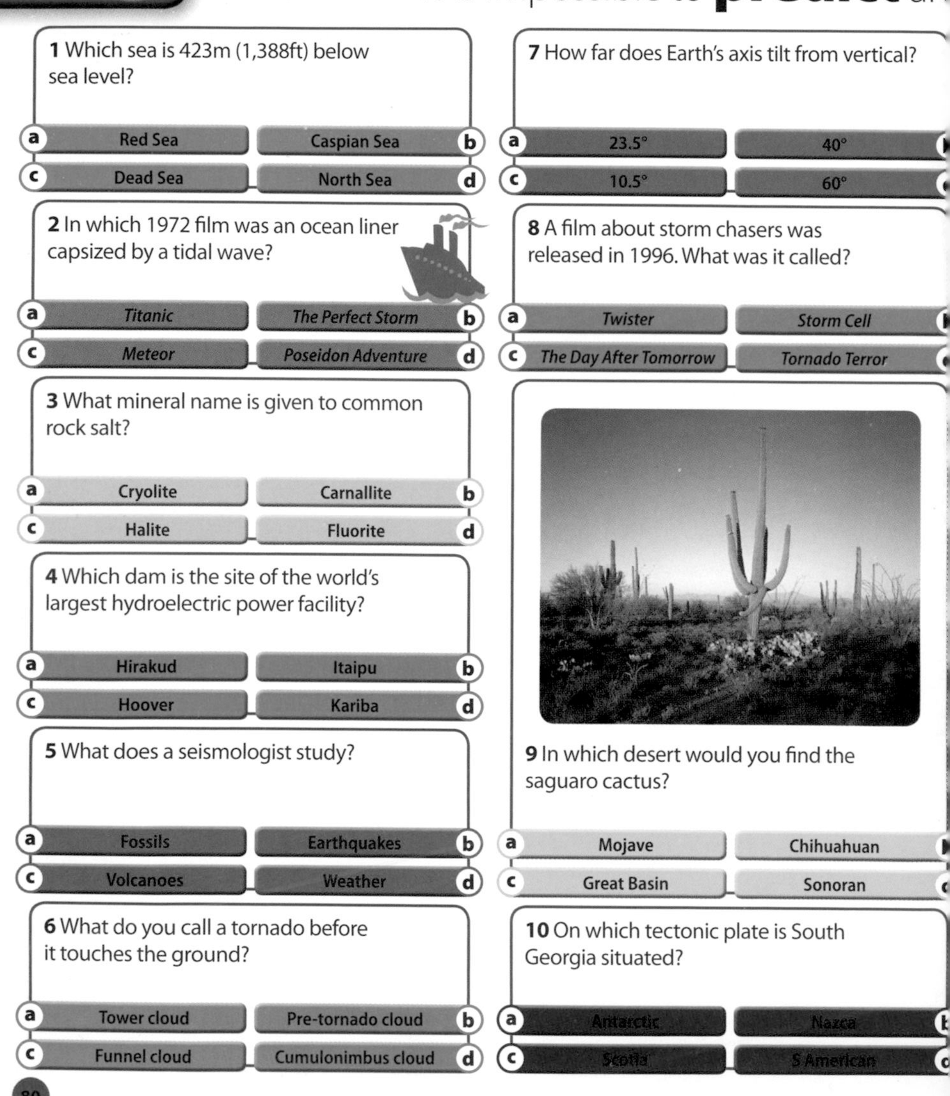

9 In which desert would you find the saguaro cactus?

- **a** Mojave
- **b** Chihuahuan
- **c** Great Basin
- **d** Sonoran

10 On which tectonic plate is South Georgia situated?

- **a** Antarctic
- **b** Nazca
- **c** Scotia
- **d** S American

impending **earthquake**

Difficulty level: **Medium**

11 The Soufrière Hills volcano has made most of which Caribbean island uninhabitable?

a Montserrat
b Bahamas
c Jamaica
d Trinidad

12 The different layers in a soil profile are called what?

a Levels
b Horizons
c Strata
d Bands

13 The biggest volcano in the world is…

a Mount St Helens
b Mauna Loa
c Mauna Kea
d Mount Vesuvius

14 Which is the equivalent of the northern lights in the southern hemisphere?

a *Aurora occidentalis*
b *Aurora australis*
c *Aurora borealis*
d *Aurora orientalis*

15 Garnets are common in which type of rock?

a Metamorphic
b Sedimentary
c Extrusive igneous
d Intrusive igneous

16 The Flow Country contains the best blanket bogs in the world. Where is it?

a Poland
b France
c Scotland
d Hungary

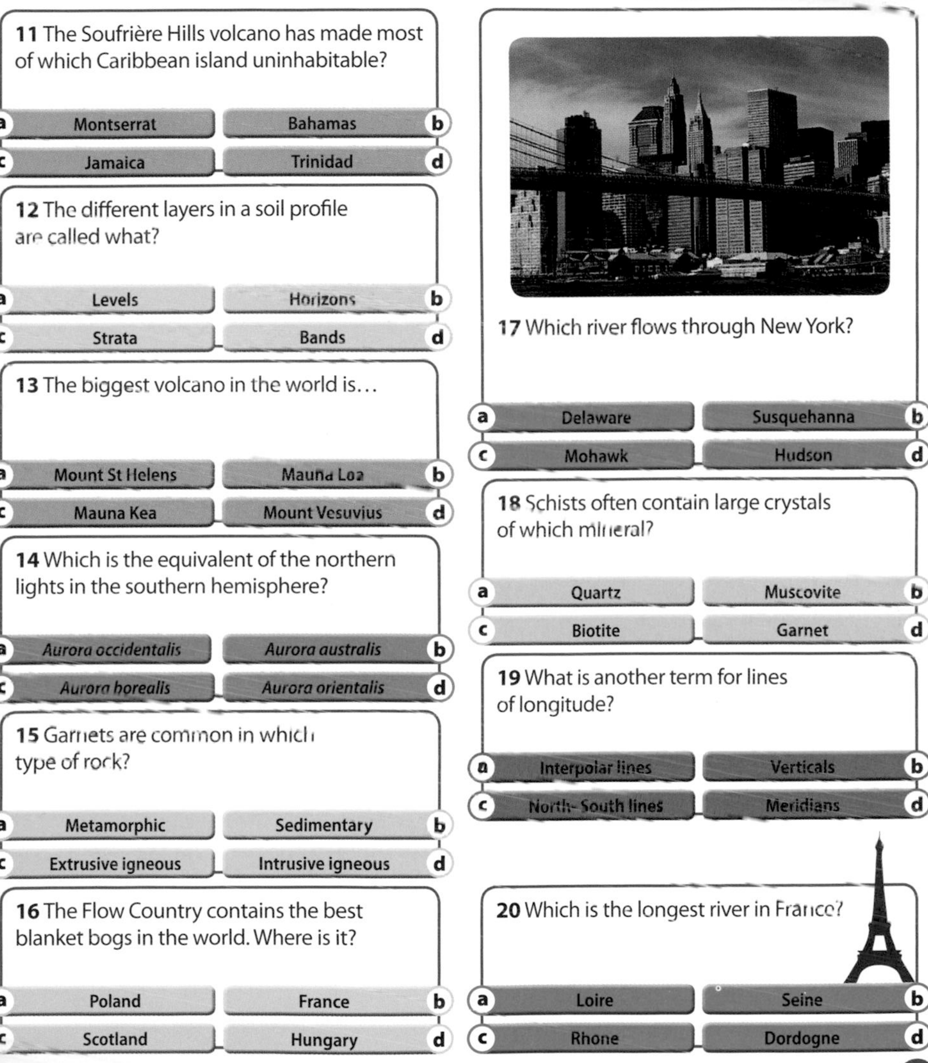

17 Which river flows through New York?

a Delaware
b Susquehanna
c Mohawk
d Hudson

18 Schists often contain large crystals of which mineral?

a Quartz
b Muscovite
c Biotite
d Garnet

19 What is another term for lines of longitude?

a Interpolar lines
b Verticals
c North–South lines
d Meridians

20 Which is the longest river in France?

a Loire
b Seine
c Rhone
d Dordogne

Lake Baikal in Russia is the

1 Which of the following is the most energy-efficient light source?

- a Compact fluorescent lamp
- b Oil lamp
- c Candle
- d Metal filament light bulb

2 Where is the active volcano Erebus?

- a Antarctica
- b Chile
- c South Georgia
- d Argentina

3 Where does the world's largest sapphire come from?

- a Sri Lanka
- b India
- c Pakistan
- d Afghanistan

4 Where are the Biebrza Marshes?

- a France
- b Scotland
- c Poland
- d Hungary

5 Which deep-ocean submersible was used by the scientists who discovered the first black smokers?

- a Cyana
- b Argo
- c Trieste
- d Alvin

6 Which term is used to describe an underwater plain at depths greater than 3,000m (9,850ft)?

- a Deep ocean plain
- b Dark plain
- c Salt plain
- d Abyssal plain

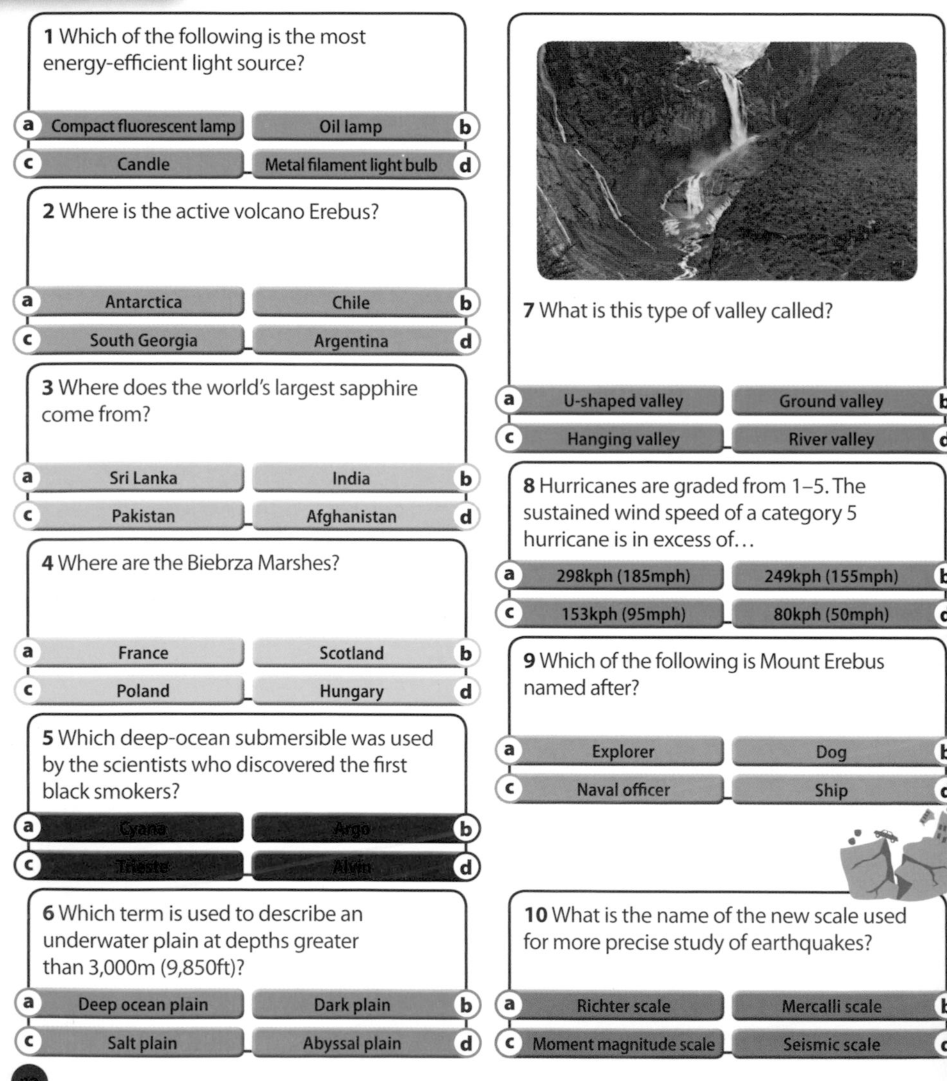

7 What is this type of valley called?

- a U-shaped valley
- b Ground valley
- c Hanging valley
- d River valley

8 Hurricanes are graded from 1–5. The sustained wind speed of a category 5 hurricane is in excess of…

- a 298kph (185mph)
- b 249kph (155mph)
- c 153kph (95mph)
- d 80kph (50mph)

9 Which of the following is Mount Erebus named after?

- a Explorer
- b Dog
- c Naval officer
- d Ship

10 What is the name of the new scale used for more precise study of earthquakes?

- a Richter scale
- b Mercalli scale
- c Moment magnitude scale
- d Seismic scale

deepest lake in the world

Difficulty level: **Hard**

11 Which type of delta has formed at the mouth of the Nile?

a Fan (arcuate)
b Cuspate
c Lacustrine
d Bird's foot

12 Which is the largest island in Antarctica?

a King George
b Alexander
c Ross
d Elephant

13 What is the upper part of a glacier known as?

a Head
b Accumulation zone
c Ablation zone
d White zone

14 Where were the earthquake and tsunami that led to the establishment of the Pacific Tsunami Warning Center?

a Gulf Islands
b Aleutian Islands
c California
d Hawaii

15 Which volcanic cone does not form part of Mount Kilimanjaro?

a Mawenzl
b Shira
c Batian
d Kibo

16 Which of the following is not a type of gneiss?

a Folded
b Augen
c Biotite
d Kyanite

17 Where are the so-called horse latitudes?

a 50–55°N and S
b 20–25°N and S
c 30–35°N and S
d 40–45°N and S

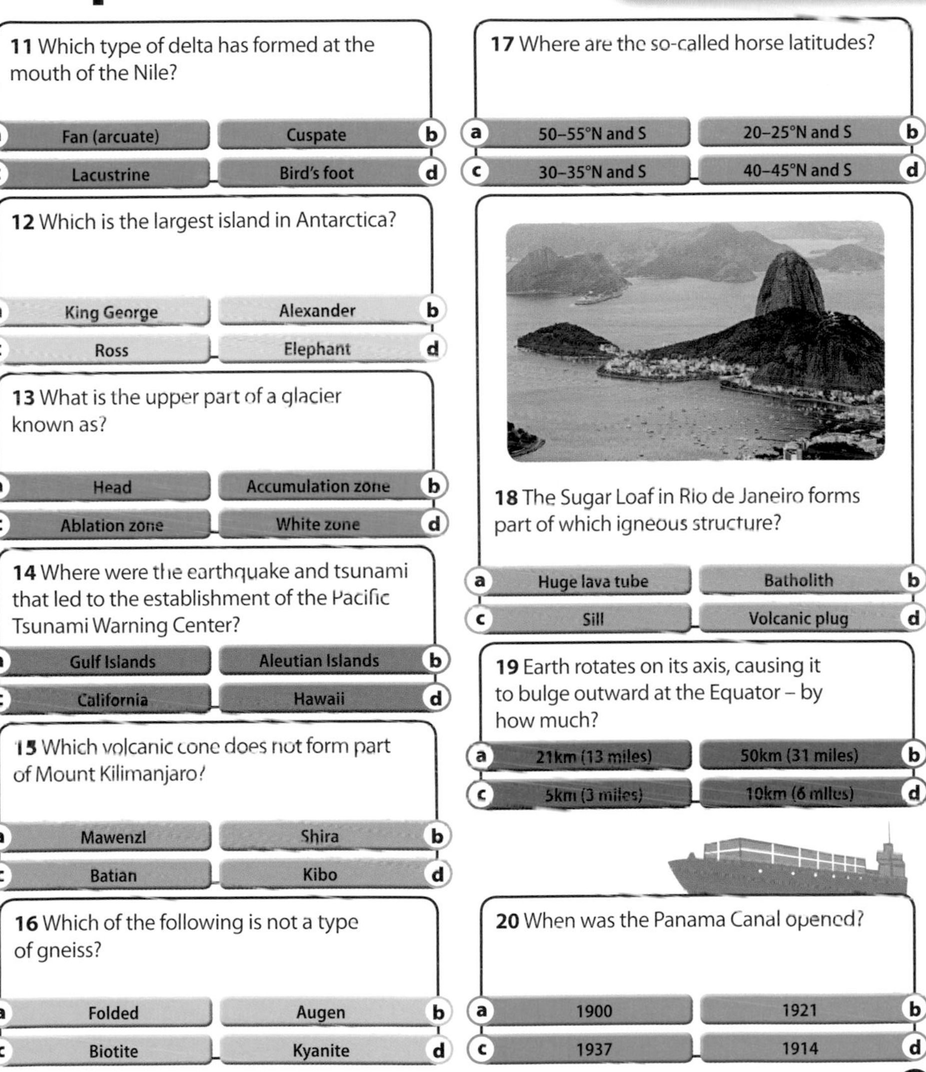

18 The Sugar Loaf in Rio de Janeiro forms part of which igneous structure?

a Huge lava tube
b Batholith
c Sill
d Volcanic plug

19 Earth rotates on its axis, causing it to bulge outward at the Equator – by how much?

a 21km (13 miles)
b 50km (31 miles)
c 5km (3 miles)
d 10km (6 miles)

20 When was the Panama Canal opened?

a 1900
b 1921
c 1937
d 1914

Quiz 40

Bracken Cave, Texas, is **home** to

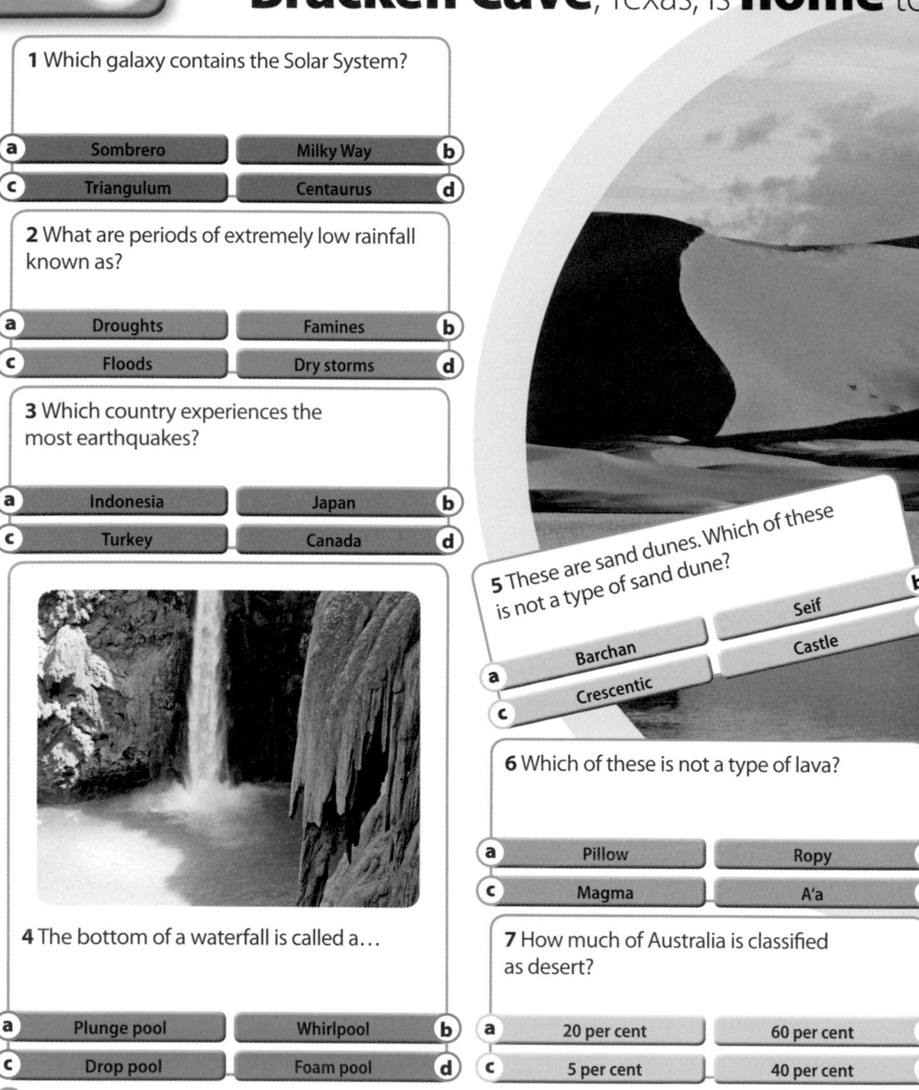

1 Which galaxy contains the Solar System?

a Sombrero
b Milky Way
c Triangulum
d Centaurus

2 What are periods of extremely low rainfall known as?

a Droughts
b Famines
c Floods
d Dry storms

3 Which country experiences the most earthquakes?

a Indonesia
b Japan
c Turkey
d Canada

4 The bottom of a waterfall is called a…

a Plunge pool
b Whirlpool
c Drop pool
d Foam pool

5 These are sand dunes. Which of these is not a type of sand dune?

a Barchan
b Seif
c Crescentic
d Castle

6 Which of these is not a type of lava?

a Pillow
b Ropy
c Magma
d A'a

7 How much of Australia is classified as desert?

a 20 per cent
b 60 per cent
c 5 per cent
d 40 per cent

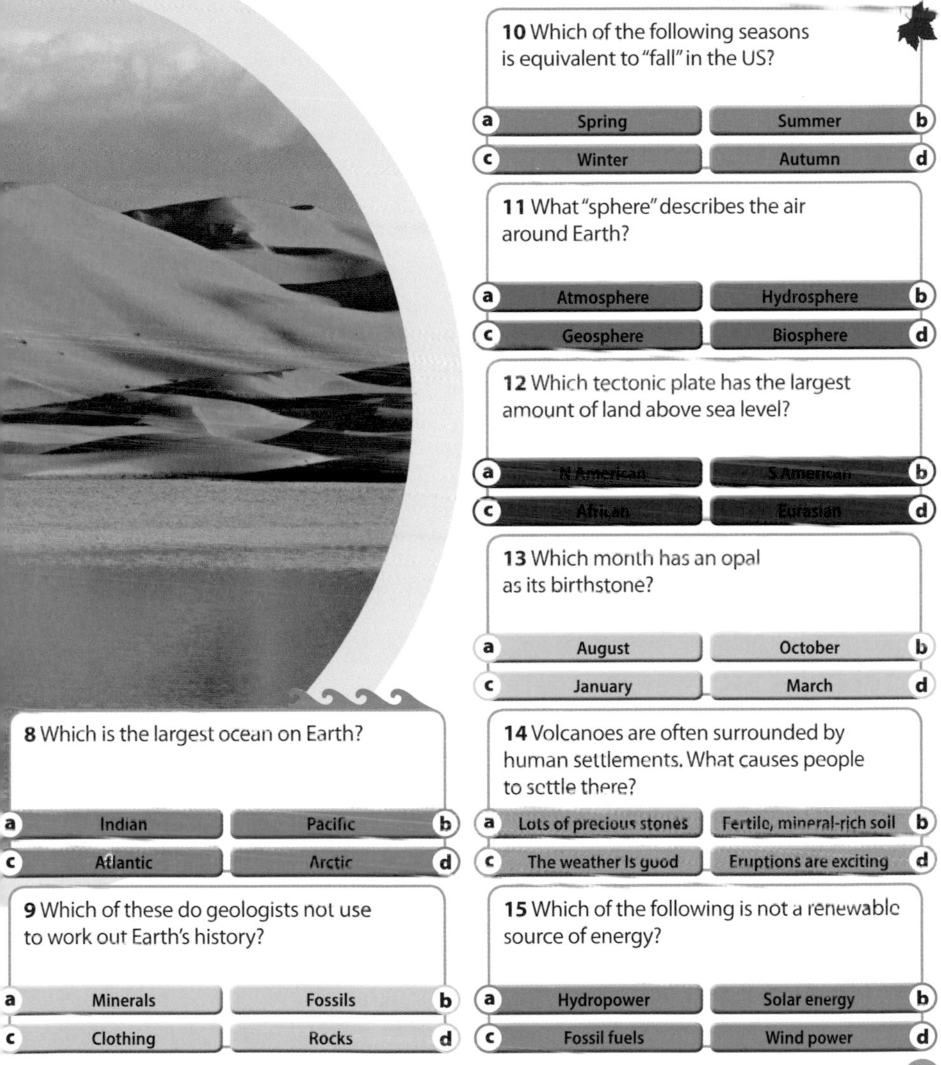

8 Which is the largest ocean on Earth?

a Indian
b Pacific
c Atlantic
d Arctic

9 Which of these do geologists not use to work out Earth's history?

a Minerals
b Fossils
c Clothing
d Rocks

10 Which of the following seasons is equivalent to "fall" in the US?

a Spring
b Summer
c Winter
d Autumn

11 What "sphere" describes the air around Earth?

a Atmosphere
b Hydrosphere
c Geosphere
d Biosphere

12 Which tectonic plate has the largest amount of land above sea level?

a N American
b S American
c African
d Eurasian

13 Which month has an opal as its birthstone?

a August
b October
c January
d March

14 Volcanoes are often surrounded by human settlements. What causes people to settle there?

a Lots of precious stones
b Fertile, mineral-rich soil
c The weather is good
d Eruptions are exciting

15 Which of the following is not a renewable source of energy?

a Hydropower
b Solar energy
c Fossil fuels
d Wind power

Quiz **41**

The Mackenzie, Canada's longest

1 In which year was the Northwest Passage ice-free for the first time since satellite records began?

a 2010
b 2008
c 2007
d 2005

2 Lyell's idea that geological processes happen at the same rate today as they did in the past is called what?

a Uniformitarianism
b Sameness
c Universality
d Uniformity

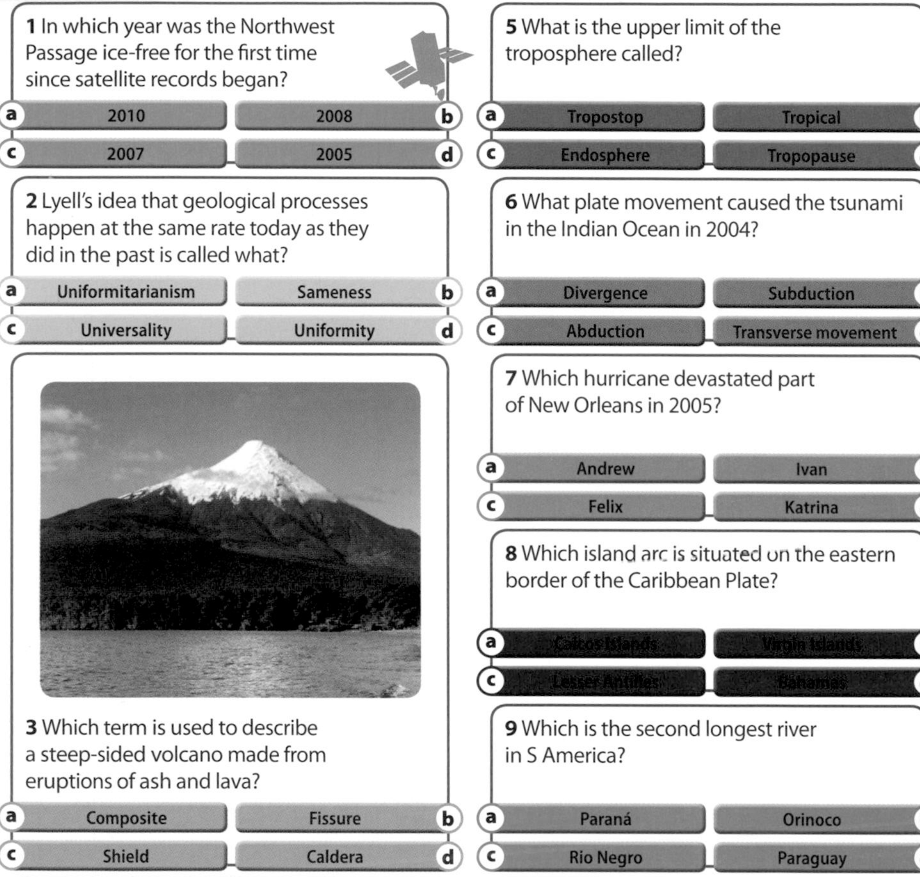

3 Which term is used to describe a steep-sided volcano made from eruptions of ash and lava?

a Composite
b Fissure
c Shield
d Caldera

4 Which US state is referred to as the Silver State?

a Oregon
b Nevada
c Utah
d Wyoming

5 What is the upper limit of the troposphere called?

a Tropostop
b Tropical
c Endosphere
d Tropopause

6 What plate movement caused the tsunami in the Indian Ocean in 2004?

a Divergence
b Subduction
c Abduction
d Transverse movement

7 Which hurricane devastated part of New Orleans in 2005?

a Andrew
b Ivan
c Felix
d Katrina

8 Which island arc is situated on the eastern border of the Caribbean Plate?

a Caicos Islands
b Virgin Islands
c Lesser Antilles
d Bahamas

9 Which is the second longest river in S America?

a Paraná
b Orinoco
c Rio Negro
d Paraguay

10 Which volcano erupted catastrophically in the second millennium BCE and is associated with the legend of Atlantis?

a Mount Vesuvius
b Krakatoa
c Kilauea
d Santorini

11 Which of the following is not part of Niagara Falls?

- a Horseshoe Falls
- b Bridal Veil Falls
- c Athabasca Falls
- d America Falls

12 How many phases are there in a lunar month?

- a 8
- b 6
- c 2
- d 10

13 Which scale is used to measure the strength of a tornado?

- a Enhanced Fujita
- b Richter
- c Saffir–Simpson
- d Beaufort

14 Which antelope, living in the Okavango Delta, has splayed hooves for walking on soft, muddy ground?

- a Tsessebe
- b Sitatunga
- c Impala
- d Sable

15 The longest river in Australia is named after which two explorers?

- a Cook and Darwin
- b Murray and Darling
- c Burke and Wills
- d Scott and Shackleton

16 Which mineral is used to make imitation diamonds?

- a Beryl
- b Hessonite
- c Titanite
- d Zircon

17 What is the volcano on Tenerife called?

- a Cumbre Vieja
- b Montañas del Fuego
- c El Teide
- d El Heirro

18 Which is the most commercially important river in W Europe?

- a Somme
- b Loire
- c Seine
- d Rhine

19 What needs to happen for fulgurite to form?

- a Mountain building
- b Volcanic eruption
- c Lightning strike
- d Sudden high pressure

20 When was the theory of plate tectonics formulated?

- a 1940s and 1950s
- b 1960s and 1970s
- c 1950s and 1960s
- d 1970s and 1980s

42 **Volcanoes** are named after **Vulcan**,

1 What are the mountains that protrude from an ice sheet called?

- **a** Terminus
- **b** Nunataks
- **c** Ridges
- **d** Rocks

2 Which harmful material can be made from a fibrous serpentinite mineral?

- **a** Soapstone
- **b** Stainless steel
- **c** Aluminium
- **d** Asbestos

3 In snow-covered mountainous areas, what can be triggered by sudden noises or thawing?

- **a** Avalanches
- **b** Flooding
- **c** Erosion
- **d** Earthquakes

4 Where in the ocean were black smokers first discovered?

- **a** By the Lesser Antilles
- **b** Around the Azores
- **c** Around Hawaii
- **d** By the Galapagos Islands

5 About how much would the world's oceans rise if the Greenland ice sheet melted?

- **a** 7.3m (24ft)
- **b** 3m (10ft)
- **c** 15m (49ft)
- **d** 10m (33ft)

6 Where was the most powerful earthquake ever recorded on Earth?

- **a** Kobe
- **b** Tangshan
- **c** Valdivia
- **d** San Francisco

7 Which wetland has Lake Drummond at its centre?

- **a** Pantanal
- **b** Great Dismal Swamp
- **c** Llanos
- **d** Everglades

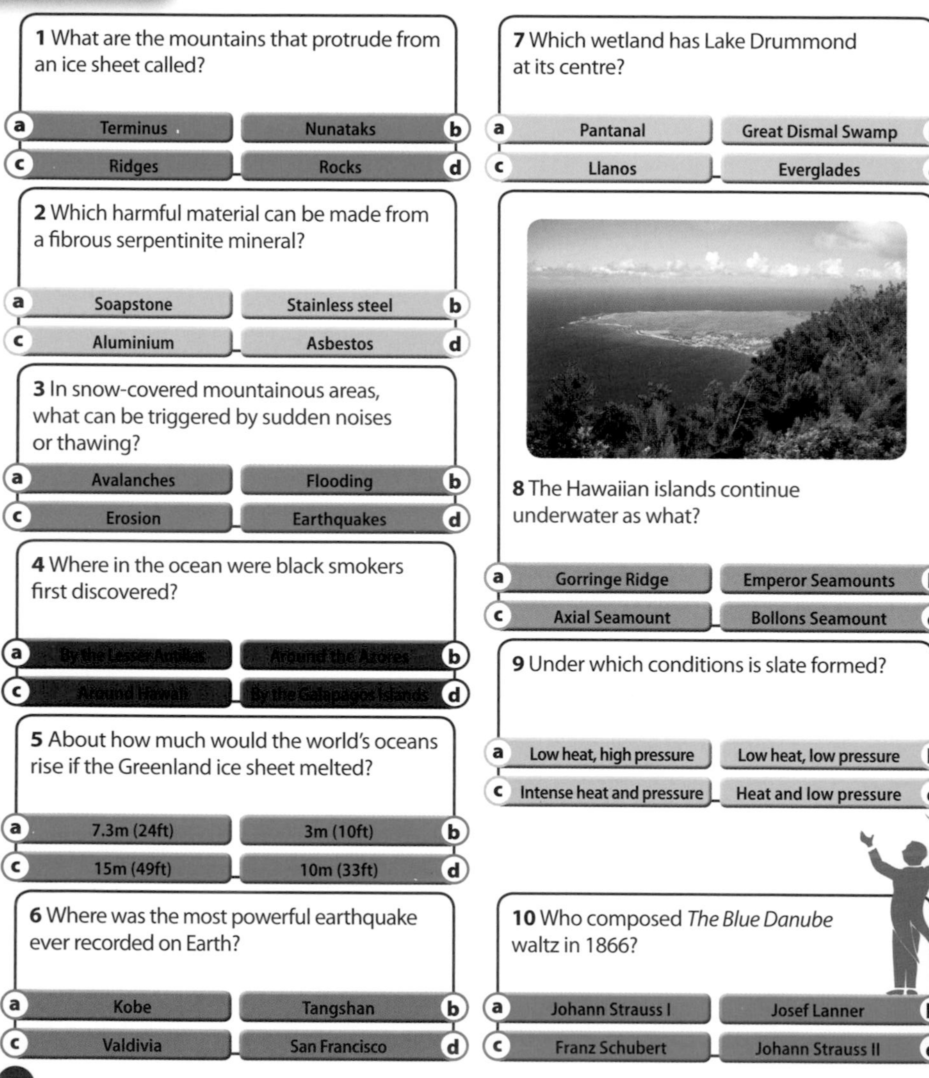

8 The Hawaiian islands continue underwater as what?

- **a** Gorringe Ridge
- **b** Emperor Seamounts
- **c** Axial Seamount
- **d** Bollons Seamount

9 Under which conditions is slate formed?

- **a** Low heat, high pressure
- **b** Low heat, low pressure
- **c** Intense heat and pressure
- **d** Heat and low pressure

10 Who composed *The Blue Danube* waltz in 1866?

- **a** Johann Strauss I
- **b** Josef Lanner
- **c** Franz Schubert
- **d** Johann Strauss II

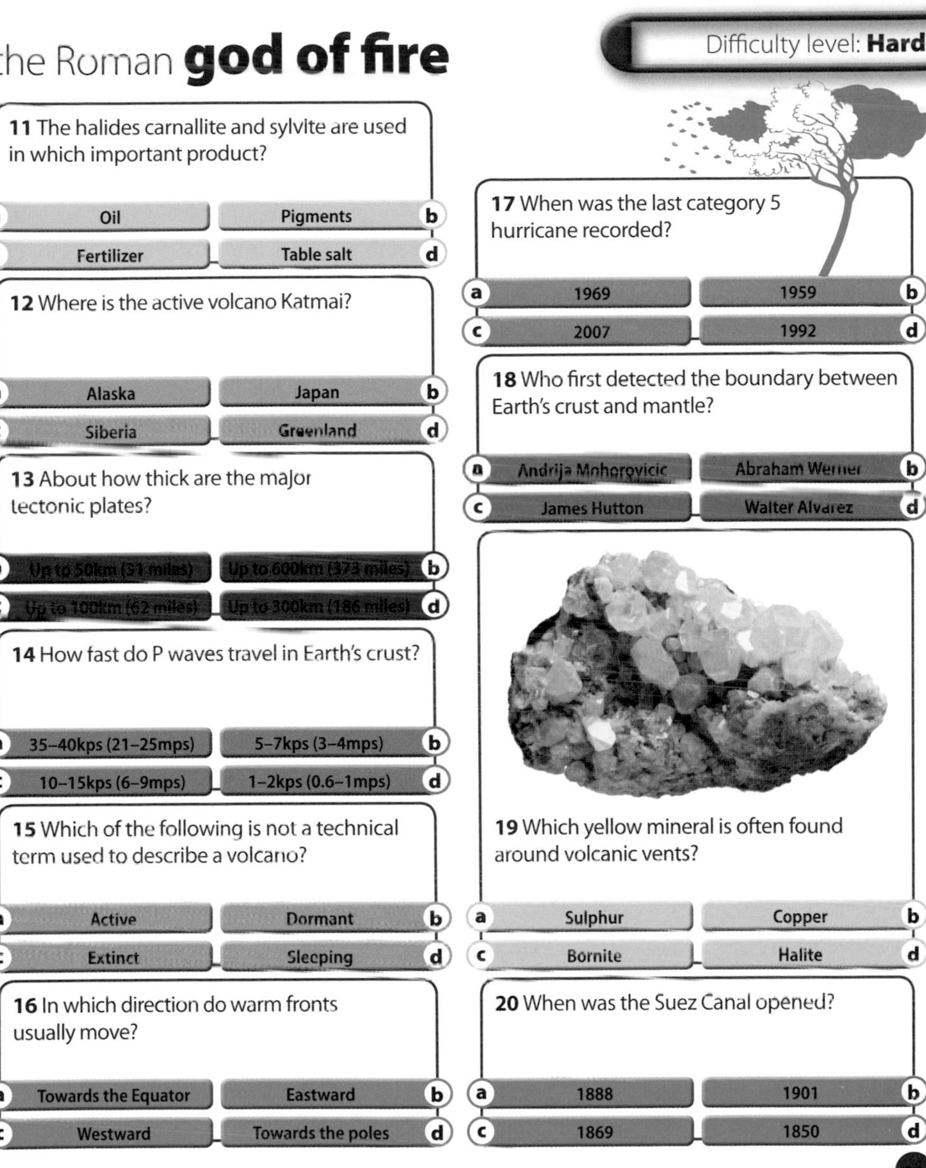

11 The halides carnallite and sylvite are used in which important product?

a Oil
b Pigments
c Fertilizer
d Table salt

12 Where is the active volcano Katmai?

a Alaska
b Japan
c Siberia
d Greenland

13 About how thick are the major tectonic plates?

a Up to 50km (31 miles)
b Up to 600km (373 miles)
c Up to 100km (62 miles)
d Up to 300km (186 miles)

14 How fast do P waves travel in Earth's crust?

a 35–40kps (21–25mps)
b 5–7kps (3–4mps)
c 10–15kps (6–9mps)
d 1–2kps (0.6–1mps)

15 Which of the following is not a technical term used to describe a volcano?

a Active
b Dormant
c Extinct
d Sleeping

16 In which direction do warm fronts usually move?

a Towards the Equator
b Eastward
c Westward
d Towards the poles

17 When was the last category 5 hurricane recorded?

a 1969
b 1959
c 2007
d 1992

18 Who first detected the boundary between Earth's crust and mantle?

a Andrija Mohorovicic
b Abraham Werner
c James Hutton
d Walter Alvarez

19 Which yellow mineral is often found around volcanic vents?

a Sulphur
b Copper
c Bornite
d Halite

20 When was the Suez Canal opened?

a 1888
b 1901
c 1869
d 1850

Quiz 43

Water can **dissolve** more

1 Which of the following is a trace fossil?

a Animal dropping
b Tooth
c Footprint
d Shell

2 Where do earthquakes usually occur?

a On the sea bed
Edge of plate boundaries
c Middle of tectonic plates
On high mountains

3 Which is the highest peak in the Rocky Mountains?

a Mount Logan
Mount Whitney
c Mount McKinley
Mount St Helens

4 In which US state is the Great Salt Lake?

a Montana
Arizona
c Utah
d Nevada

5 Which of these volcanoes is not in Mexico?

a Popocatépetl
Paricutin
c El Chichón
Mount Fuji

6 Parts of which desert, shown here, have had no rain at all since records began?

a Patagonian
b Atacama
c Sahara
Gobi

7 In which layer of a rainforest does a sloth spend most of its time?

8 Which planet is nearest to the Sun?

9 Which of the following is not a type of rock?

10 The atmosphere contains most of which gas?

11 When pollution and fog mix, what is created?

12 Which tectonic plate has the second largest amount of land above sea level?

13 This is the Hoover Dam. How much of the world's electricity is provided by dams built on rivers?

14 Which of the following is not true of coniferous trees?

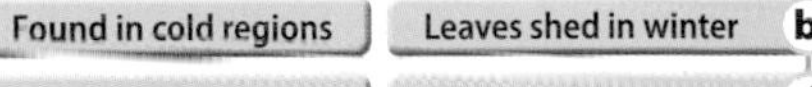

15 Which is the birthstone for September?

a Garnet | Diamond b

c Pearl | Sapphire d

There are **no bridges** over

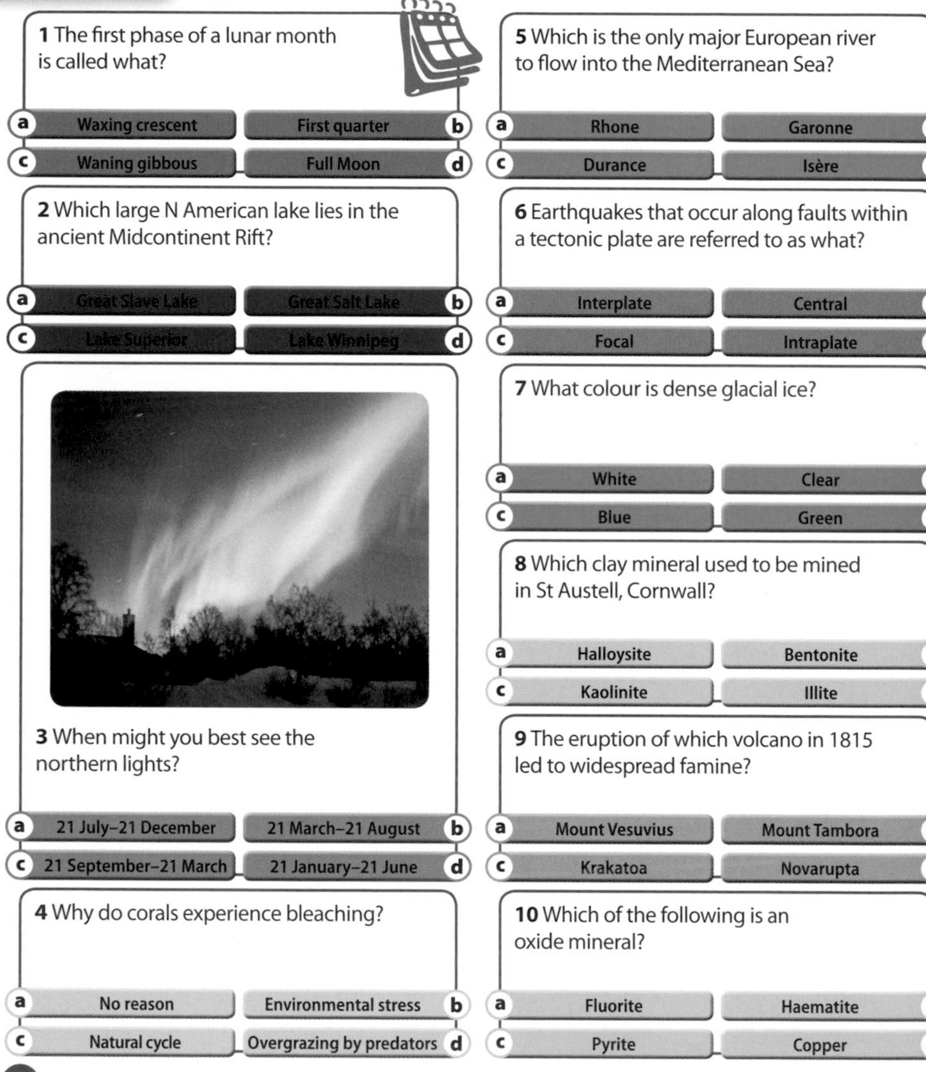

1 The first phase of a lunar month is called what?

a Waxing crescent
b First quarter
c Waning gibbous
d Full Moon

2 Which large N American lake lies in the ancient Midcontinent Rift?

a Great Slave Lake
b Great Salt Lake
c Lake Superior
d Lake Winnipeg

3 When might you best see the northern lights?

a 21 July–21 December
b 21 March–21 August
c 21 September–21 March
d 21 January–21 June

4 Why do corals experience bleaching?

a No reason
b Environmental stress
c Natural cycle
d Overgrazing by predators

5 Which is the only major European river to flow into the Mediterranean Sea?

a Rhone
b Garonne
c Durance
d Isère

6 Earthquakes that occur along faults within a tectonic plate are referred to as what?

a Interplate
b Central
c Focal
d Intraplate

7 What colour is dense glacial ice?

a White
b Clear
c Blue
d Green

8 Which clay mineral used to be mined in St Austell, Cornwall?

a Halloysite
b Bentonite
c Kaolinite
d Illite

9 The eruption of which volcano in 1815 led to widespread famine?

a Mount Vesuvius
b Mount Tambora
c Krakatoa
d Novarupta

10 Which of the following is an oxide mineral?

a Fluorite
b Haematite
c Pyrite
d Copper

11 On which line of latitude is the Arctic?

a 23° 26′ 16″ N
b 23° 26′ 16″ S
c 66° 33′ 44″ S
d 66° 33′ 44″ N

12 Weather only occurs in one layer of the atmosphere. Which one?

a Troposphere
b Stratosphere
c Mesosphere
d Thermosphere

13 What does fulgurite mean in Latin?

a Flash of light
b Shooting star
c Meteor
d Thunderbolt

14 What percentage of the world's glaciers are in Antarctica?

a 80 per cent
b 70 per cent
c 60 per cent
d 90 per cent

15 Which scale is used to measure the strength of a hurricane?

a Fujita
b Saffir-Simpson
c Richter
d Beaufort

16 At the mouth of which river are the Coorong wetlands?

a Murrumbidgee
b Flinders
c Murray
d Darling

17 Which term describes the point where two rivers meet?

a River junction
b Source
c Spring
d Confluence

18 Who was the Roman god of fire and volcanoes?

a Vulcan
b Hephaestus
c Adranus
d Nusku

19 Which is not a form of physical weathering of rocks?

a Dissolving in rainwater
b Freeze-thaw of water
c Infiltration by plants
d Heating and cooling

20 What is the name for a large movement of water formed by the funnelling of an incoming tide into a river?

a Storm surge
b Tidal bore
c Tsunami
d Rogue wave

45

About **4,000** naturally occurring minerals

1 In which direction do cold and occluded fronts generally move?

a Towards the Equator
b Towards the poles
c West to east
d East to west

2 The top of Table Mountain is made of which stone?

a Basalt
b Sandstone
c Limestone
d Granite

3 Which type of volcano was Mount Kenya?

a Cinder cone
b Stratovolcano
c Shield
d Dome

4 If both the West and East Antarctic ice sheets melted, by about how much would global sea levels rise?

a 88m (289ft)
b 58m (190ft)
c 29m (95ft)
d 104m (341ft)

5 Which mountain is it said that Noah's Ark landed on?

a Mount Fuji
b Mount St Helens
c Mount Ararat
d Mount Kilimanjaro

6 Which layer of the atmosphere is immediately below the thermosphere?

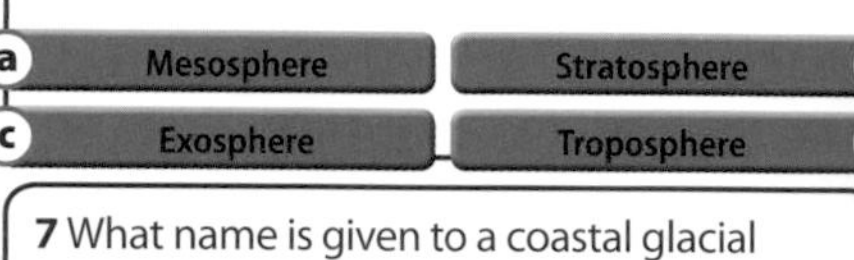

a Mesosphere
b Stratosphere
c Exosphere
d Troposphere

7 What name is given to a coastal glacial valley that has been flooded by a rise in sea level?

a Estuary
b Mouth
c Fjord
d Ria

8 Which wetland is drained by the Suwannee River?

a Hortobágy
b Biebrza Marshes
c Okefenokee Swamp
d Waituna Lagoon

9 In an earthquake, what describes the sinking of buildings into water-saturated soil?

a Soil anisotropy
b Soil degradation
c Soil fractionalization
d Soil liquefaction

10 Who made the first barometer?

a Jean Borda
b Evangelista Torricelli
c Galileo Galilei
d Joseph Henry

...have been found on **Earth**

Difficulty level: **Hard**

11 Which of these minerals is an important source of uranium?

12 Which country invented emissions trading as a way of reducing greenhouse gas production?

13 Which of these organisms would you find in hot springs?

14 Which part of the N American prairies receives the least rainfall?

It varies | West **b**
East | Centre **d**

15 Where is the tallest hydroelectric dam in the world?

16 When were black smokers first discovered?

17 Mountain gorillas live on the slopes of which volcanic mountain chain?

a Virunga | Elgon **b**
c Great Karas | Kilimanjaro **d**

18 Where have the largest underwater landslides occurred?

a Pacific coast of Canada | Off the coast of Italy **b**
c Atlantic coast of Norway | Off the coast of Japan **d**

19 Which of the following is not formed through regional metamorphism?

20 Which water body occupies a depression formed by the Rift Valley?

a Arabian Sea | Persian Gulf **b**
c Dead Sea | Red Sea **d**

About 320 million years ago, **Scotland**

1 Which is the hardest mineral found on Earth?

a  b 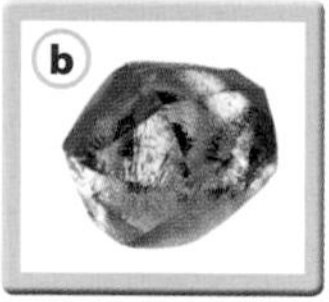 c  d

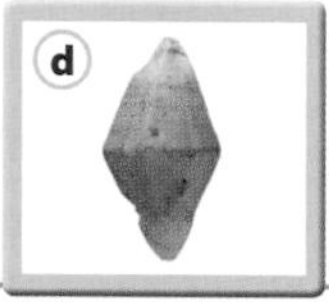

5 Which tectonic plate is the most densely populated?

a African | Eurasian
c Australian | S American

6 Which term is used to describe a small quake following the main earthquake?

a Secondary quake | Silvershock
c Aftershock | Afterquake

2 Which hazard becomes more likely after several days of snowfall?

a Lightning | Avalanche b
c Landslide | Hailstorm d

3 What is the birthstone for December?

a Topaz | Ruby b
c Peridot | Turquoise d

4 Which of the following mountain ranges is not in France?

a Vosges | Massif Central b
c Ardennes | Apennines d

7 If a storm like this forms in the Caribbean, what is it called?

a Cyclone | Super storm
c Hurricane | Typhoon

8 The weight of a glacier can make a river underneath the ice…

a Freeze
b Flood
c Flow uphill
d Flow downhill

9 Which planet is furthest from the Sun?

a Uranus
b Saturn
c Jupiter
d Neptune

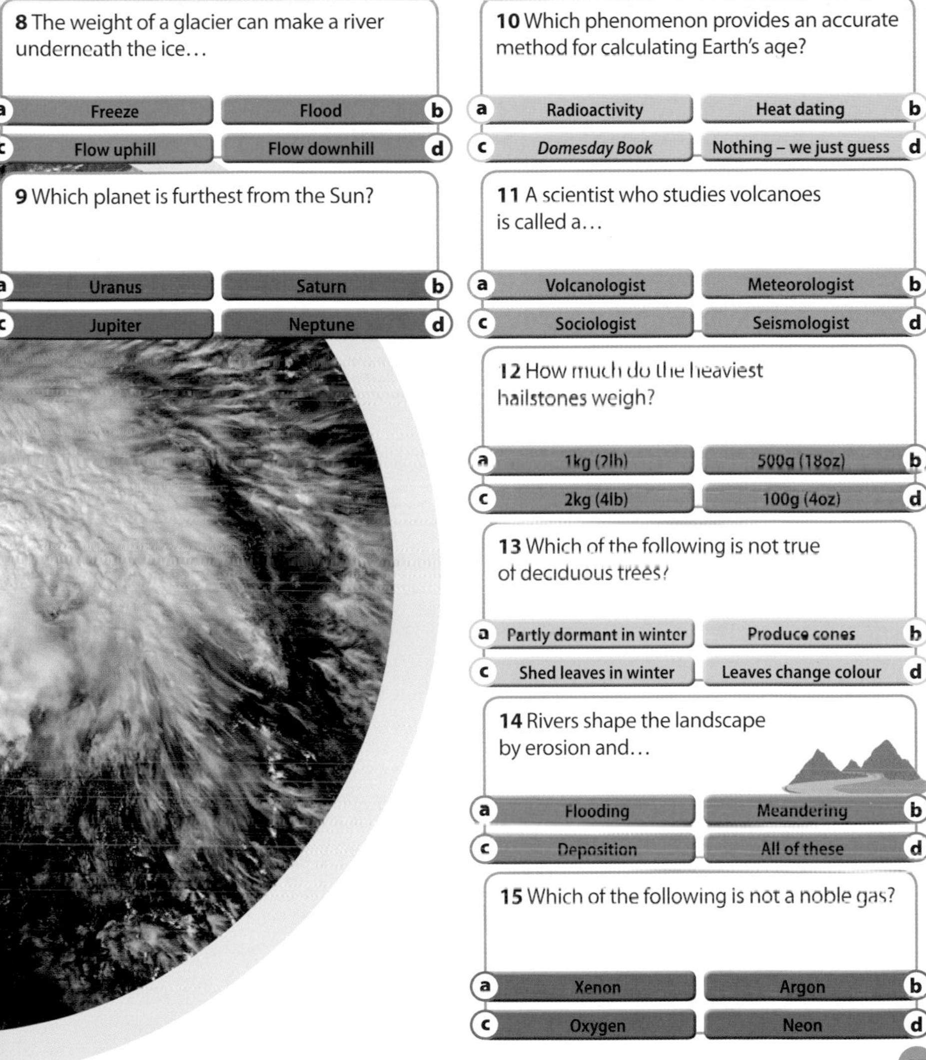

10 Which phenomenon provides an accurate method for calculating Earth's age?

a Radioactivity
b Heat dating
c *Domesday Book*
d Nothing – we just guess

11 A scientist who studies volcanoes is called a…

a Volcanologist
b Meteorologist
c Sociologist
d Seismologist

12 How much do the heaviest hailstones weigh?

a 1kg (2lb)
b 500g (18oz)
c 2kg (4lb)
d 100g (4oz)

13 Which of the following is not true of deciduous trees?

a Partly dormant in winter
b Produce cones
c Shed leaves in winter
d Leaves change colour

14 Rivers shape the landscape by erosion and…

a Flooding
b Meandering
c Deposition
d All of these

15 Which of the following is not a noble gas?

a Xenon
b Argon
c Oxygen
d Neon

Quiz 47

The **driest** desert on **Earth**

1 What happens when water freezes and forms ice?

- a It expands
- b It shrinks
- c It absorbs air
- d It changes colour

2 Which of the following is a halide mineral?

- a Halite
- b Rutile
- c Staurolite
- d Magnetite

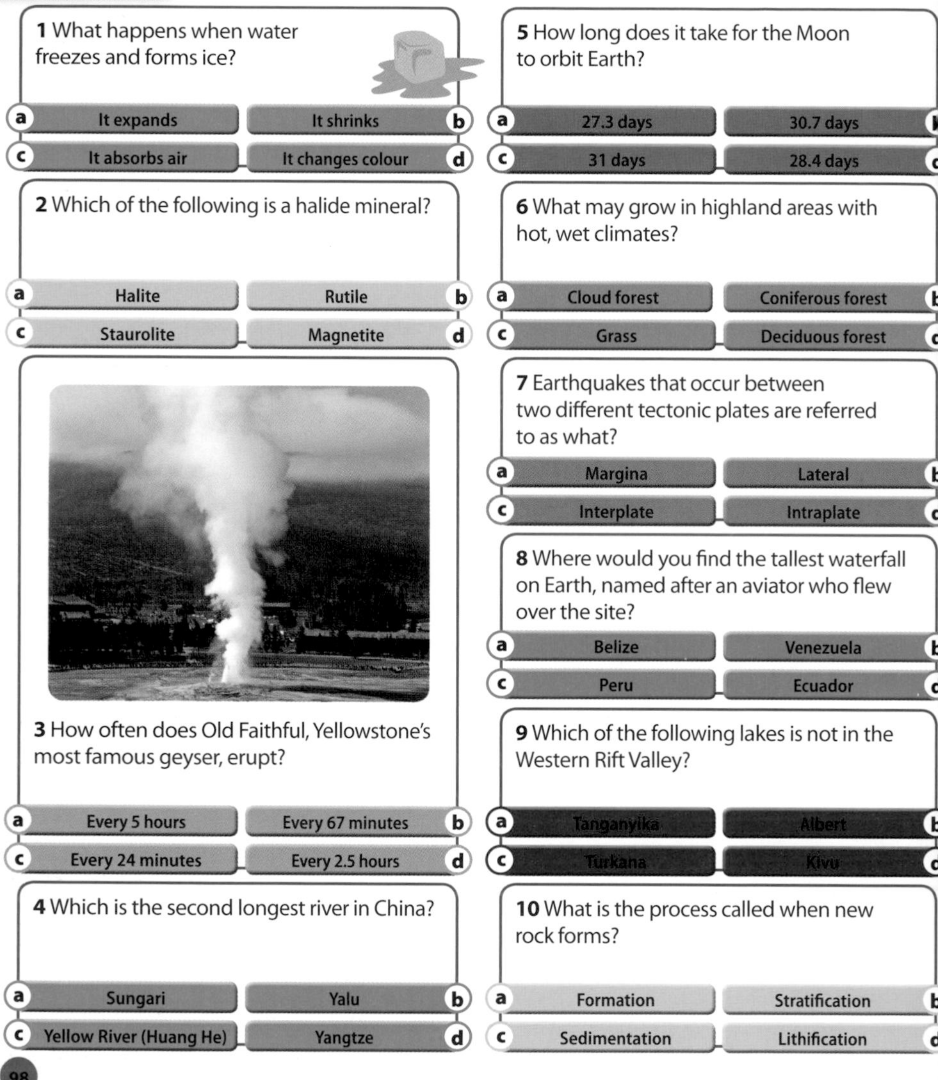

3 How often does Old Faithful, Yellowstone's most famous geyser, erupt?

- a Every 5 hours
- b Every 67 minutes
- c Every 24 minutes
- d Every 2.5 hours

4 Which is the second longest river in China?

- a Sungari
- b Yalu
- c Yellow River (Huang He)
- d Yangtze

5 How long does it take for the Moon to orbit Earth?

- a 27.3 days
- b 30.7 days
- c 31 days
- d 28.4 days

6 What may grow in highland areas with hot, wet climates?

- a Cloud forest
- b Coniferous forest
- c Grass
- d Deciduous forest

7 Earthquakes that occur between two different tectonic plates are referred to as what?

- a Margina
- b Lateral
- c Interplate
- d Intraplate

8 Where would you find the tallest waterfall on Earth, named after an aviator who flew over the site?

- a Belize
- b Venezuela
- c Peru
- d Ecuador

9 Which of the following lakes is not in the Western Rift Valley?

- a Tanganyika
- b Albert
- c Turkana
- d Kivu

10 What is the process called when new rock forms?

- a Formation
- b Stratification
- c Sedimentation
- d Lithification

11 From which rock are karst features, like these in Vietnam, formed?

- **a** Granite
- **b** Basalt
- **c** Limestone
- **d** Sandstone

12 Which chain of volcanic islands lies west of the Alaska Peninsula?

- **a** Lesser Antilles
- **b** Mariana Islands
- **c** South Sandwich Islands
- **d** Aleutian Islands

13 What colour is malachite?

- **a** Yellow
- **b** Green
- **c** Pink
- **d** Blue

14 Much of the Llanos grassland in S America is now used for what?

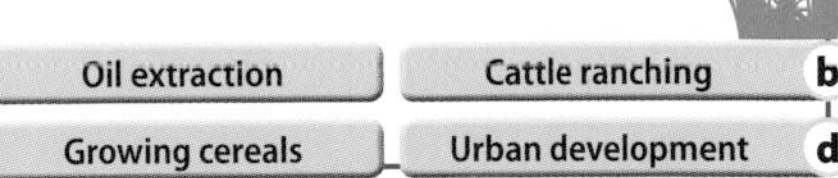

- **a** Oil extraction
- **b** Cattle ranching
- **c** Growing cereals
- **d** Urban development

15 Which is the most active volcano on Earth?

- **a** Kilauea
- **b** Etna
- **c** Surtsey
- **d** Stromboli

16 A coprolite is a fossilized…

- **a** Insect in amber
- **b** Animal burrow
- **c** Animal dropping
- **d** Bone fragment

17 On which line of latitude is the Tropic of Capricorn?

- **a** 23° 26′ 16″ N
- **b** 66° 33′ 44″ S
- **c** 0° latitude
- **d** 23° 26′ 16″ S

18 Why does weather only occur in the atmosphere closest to Earth?

- **a** Most polluted
- **b** Highest winds
- **c** Most oxygen
- **d** Most water vapour

19 Which types of seismic wave are used to locate earthquakes?

- **a** Rayleigh and P waves
- **b** P and S waves
- **c** Love and S waves
- **d** All of these

20 Which is the longest river in SE Asia?

- **a** Irrawaddy
- **b** Kwai
- **c** Chindwin
- **d** Mekong

There are about **15,000** glaciers

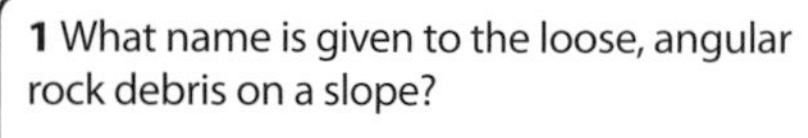

1 What name is given to the loose, angular rock debris on a slope?

a Scree
b Rubble
c Avalanche
d Boulders

2 What is the name of this famous landmark, formed by erosion?

a The Apostles
b The Needles
c Uluru
d Giant's Causeway

3 Into which sea does the Yellow River (Huang He) empty?

a Bohai Sea
b South China Sea
c Sea of Japan
d East China Sea

4 Who named the ancient continent of Gondwana?

a Henry Hess
b James Dana
c Eduard Suess
d Charles Walcott

5 Shards of which igneous rock were used by prehistoric people to make sharp weapons?

a Rhyolite
b Peridotite
c Basalt
d Obsidian

6 How fast do P waves travel in the mantle?

a 52–56kps (32–35mps)
b 8–13kps (5–8mps)
c 18–24kps (11–15mps)
d 32–38kps (20–24mps)

7 In the northern hemisphere, how does warm air flow in a cyclone?

a Clockwise, upwards
b Anticlockwise, downwards
c Clockwise, downwards
d Anticlockwise, upwards

8 Which circular depression forms from an empty magma chamber?

a Caldera
b Crater
c Cirque
d Cwm

9 Which layer of the atmosphere is immediately above the troposphere?

a Mesosphere
b Thermosphere
c Exosphere
d Stratosphere

10 Who proved that air pressure drops with increasing altitude?

a Tycho Brahe
b Johannes Kepler
c Blaise Pascal
d Evangelista Torricelli

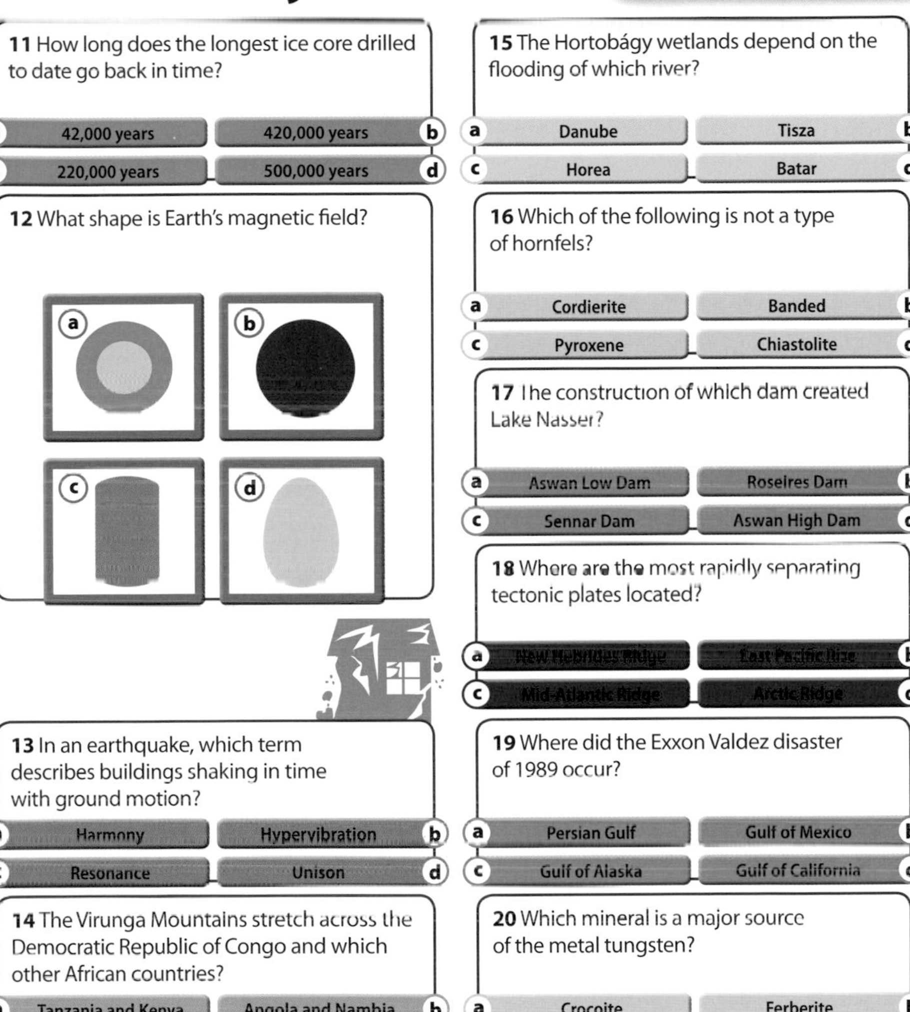

11 How long does the longest ice core drilled to date go back in time?

a 42,000 years
b 420,000 years
c 220,000 years
d 500,000 years

12 What shape is Earth's magnetic field?

a
b
c
d

13 In an earthquake, which term describes buildings shaking in time with ground motion?

a Harmony
b Hypervibration
c Resonance
d Unison

14 The Virunga Mountains stretch across the Democratic Republic of Congo and which other African countries?

a Tanzania and Kenya
b Angola and Nambia
c Zambia and Malawi
d Rwanda and Uganda

15 The Hortobágy wetlands depend on the flooding of which river?

a Danube
b Tisza
c Horea
d Batar

16 Which of the following is not a type of hornfels?

a Cordierite
b Banded
c Pyroxene
d Chiastolite

17 The construction of which dam created Lake Nasser?

a Aswan Low Dam
b Roseires Dam
c Sennar Dam
d Aswan High Dam

18 Where are the most rapidly separating tectonic plates located?

a New Hebrides Ridge
b East Pacific Rise
c Mid-Atlantic Ridge
d Arctic Ridge

19 Where did the Exxon Valdez disaster of 1989 occur?

a Persian Gulf
b Gulf of Mexico
c Gulf of Alaska
d Gulf of California

20 Which mineral is a major source of the metal tungsten?

a Crocoite
b Ferberite
c Scheelite
d Wulfenite

Quiz 49

The **oldest** exposed **rocks** in the Grand

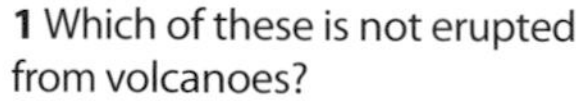

1 Which of these is not erupted from volcanoes?

a Gas
b Granite
c Ash
d Cinder

2 Where is the largest tree in the world, the giant sequoia, found?

a Montana
b Washington
c California
d Oregon

3 Which term is used to describe sustained winds of more than 64kph (40mph)?

a Breeze
b Tornado
c Gale
d Gust

4 Sedimentary rock is formed by…

a Erosion
b Lithification
c Crystal patterns
d Solidified magma

5 At what temperature is snow most likely to fall?

a –30°C (–22°F)
b Just above freezing
c –10°C (14°F)
d Just below freezing

6 Who wrote *A Journey to the Centre of the Earth* in 1874?

a Jules Verne
b Ryder Haggard
c Arthur Conan Doyle
d Rudyard Kipling

7 Which mountain chain runs the length of Italy?

a Apennines
b Pennines
c Alps
d Dolomites

8 Coral reefs are endangered by what?

a Rising levels of sediment
b Rising temperatures
c More acidic sea water
d All of these

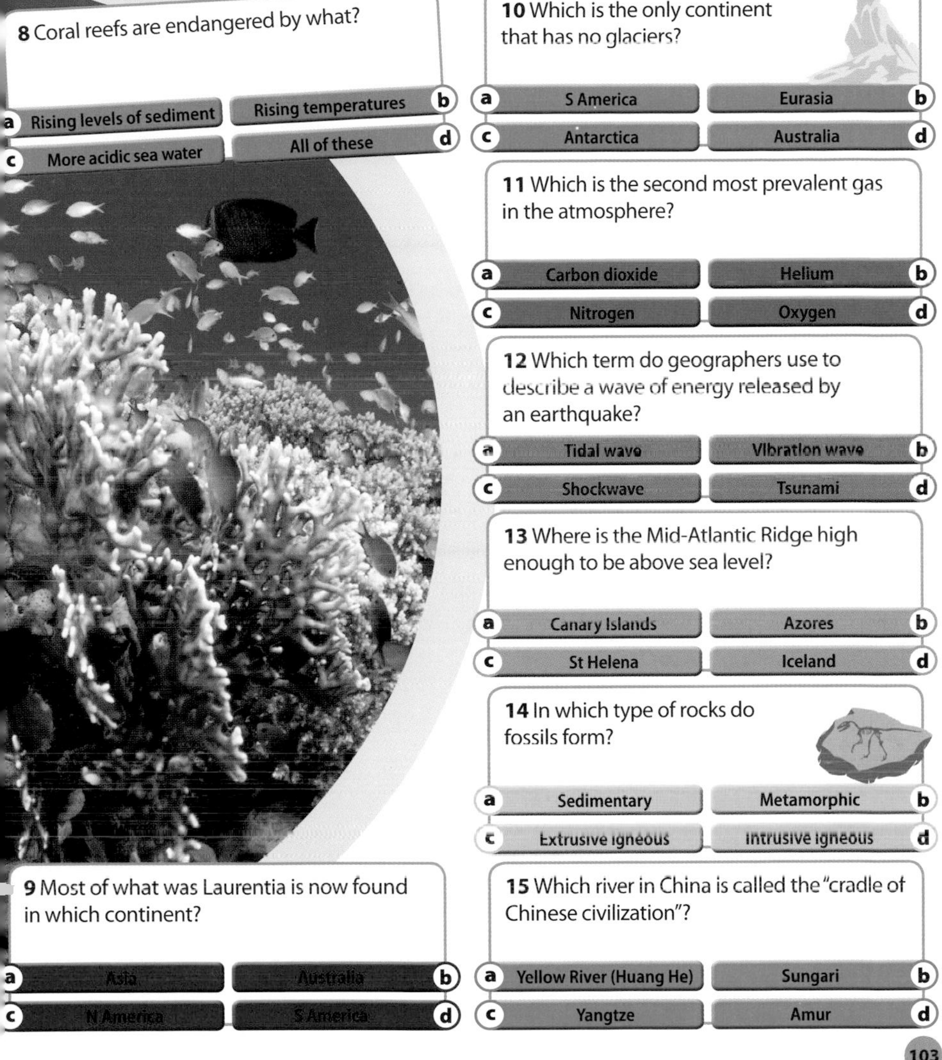

9 Most of what was Laurentia is now found in which continent?

a Asia
b Australia
c N America
d S America

10 Which is the only continent that has no glaciers?

a S America
b Eurasia
c Antarctica
d Australia

11 Which is the second most prevalent gas in the atmosphere?

a Carbon dioxide
b Helium
c Nitrogen
d Oxygen

12 Which term do geographers use to describe a wave of energy released by an earthquake?

a Tidal wave
b Vibration wave
c Shockwave
d Tsunami

13 Where is the Mid-Atlantic Ridge high enough to be above sea level?

a Canary Islands
b Azores
c St Helena
d Iceland

14 In which type of rocks do fossils form?

a Sedimentary
b Metamorphic
c Extrusive igneous
d Intrusive igneous

15 Which river in China is called the "cradle of Chinese civilization"?

a Yellow River (Huang He)
b Sungari
c Yangtze
d Amur

It takes about **1 million** cloud

1 Laurasia and Gondwana formed from the break up of which other supercontinent?

- a Pannotia
- b Pangaea
- c Rodinia
- d Eurasia

2 The Egyptian resort of Sharm El Sheikh is famous for its diving. In which sea does the diving take place?

- a Mediterranean Sea
- b Indian Ocean
- c Dead Sea
- d Red Sea

3 Which type of earthquake usually causes the most damage?

- a Medium focus
- b Deep focus
- c Shallow focus
- d All cause similar damage

4 Which of the following lakes is not in the eastern Rift Valley?

- a Naivasha
- b Nakuru
- c Edward
- d Manyara

5 Which watery region of the UK is Arthur Ransome's book *Swallows and Amazons* set in?

- a Lake District
- b Scottish Highlands
- c Norfolk
- d Peak District

6 Which of these is involved in the process of lithification?

- a Cementation
- b Compaction
- c Loss of porosity
- d All of these

7 Stromatolite fossils are found in shallow water. Where do the oldest examples come from?

- a Australia
- b Canada
- c China
- d Antarctica

8 Where is the largest borax mine in the world?

- a Ontario, Canada
- b California, US
- c Papua, Indonesia
- d Orapa, Botswana

9 Soils known as podzols are generally acidic and…

- a Fine textured
- b Lack horizons
- c Coarse textured
- d Peaty

10 What instrument is used to measure wind speed?

- a Anemometer
- b Thermometer
- c Hygrometer
- d Barometer

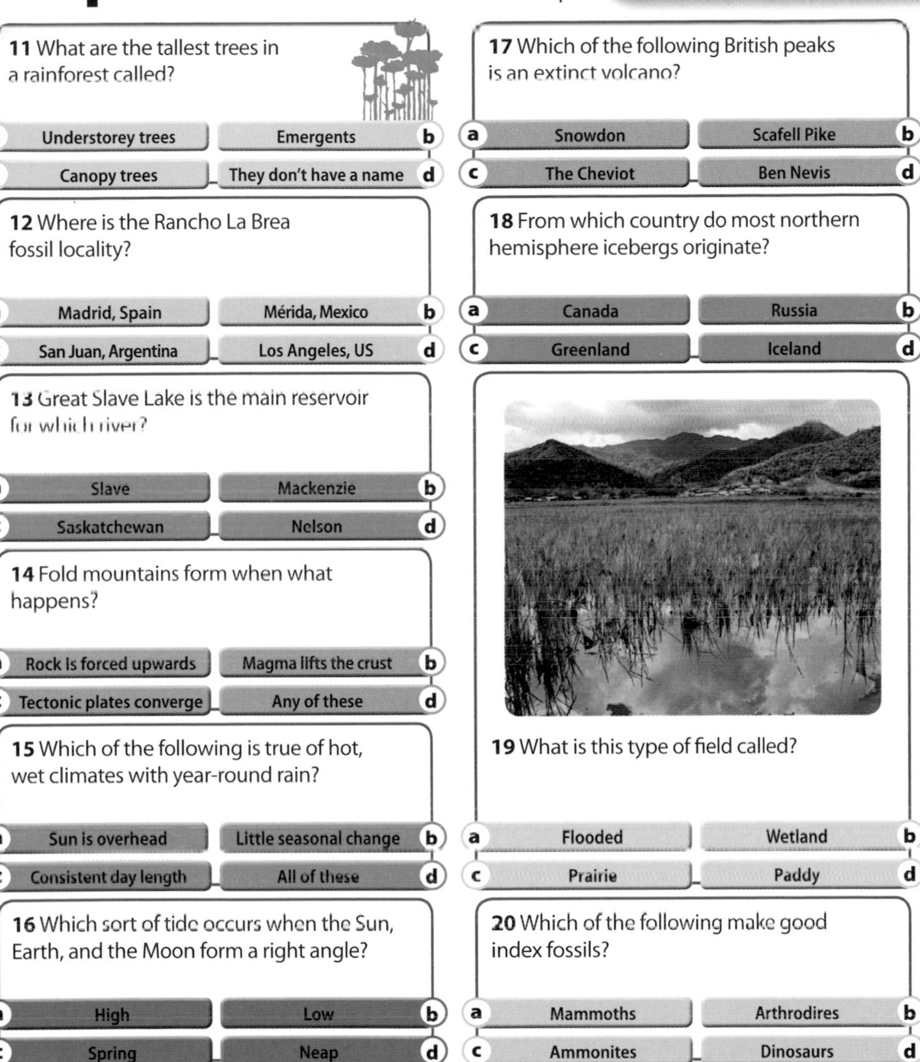

11 What are the tallest trees in a rainforest called?

a Understorey trees
b Emergents
c Canopy trees
d They don't have a name

12 Where is the Rancho La Brea fossil locality?

a Madrid, Spain
b Mérida, Mexico
c San Juan, Argentina
d Los Angeles, US

13 Great Slave Lake is the main reservoir for which river?

a Slave
b Mackenzie
c Saskatchewan
d Nelson

14 Fold mountains form when what happens?

a Rock is forced upwards
b Magma lifts the crust
c Tectonic plates converge
d Any of these

15 Which of the following is true of hot, wet climates with year-round rain?

a Sun is overhead
b Little seasonal change
c Consistent day length
d All of these

16 Which sort of tide occurs when the Sun, Earth, and the Moon form a right angle?

a High
b Low
c Spring
d Neap

17 Which of the following British peaks is an extinct volcano?

a Snowdon
b Scafell Pike
c The Cheviot
d Ben Nevis

18 From which country do most northern hemisphere icebergs originate?

a Canada
b Russia
c Greenland
d Iceland

19 What is this type of field called?

a Flooded
b Wetland
c Prairie
d Paddy

20 Which of the following make good index fossils?

a Mammoths
b Arthrodires
c Ammonites
d Dinosaurs

Quiz 51

Some people still have **houses** in

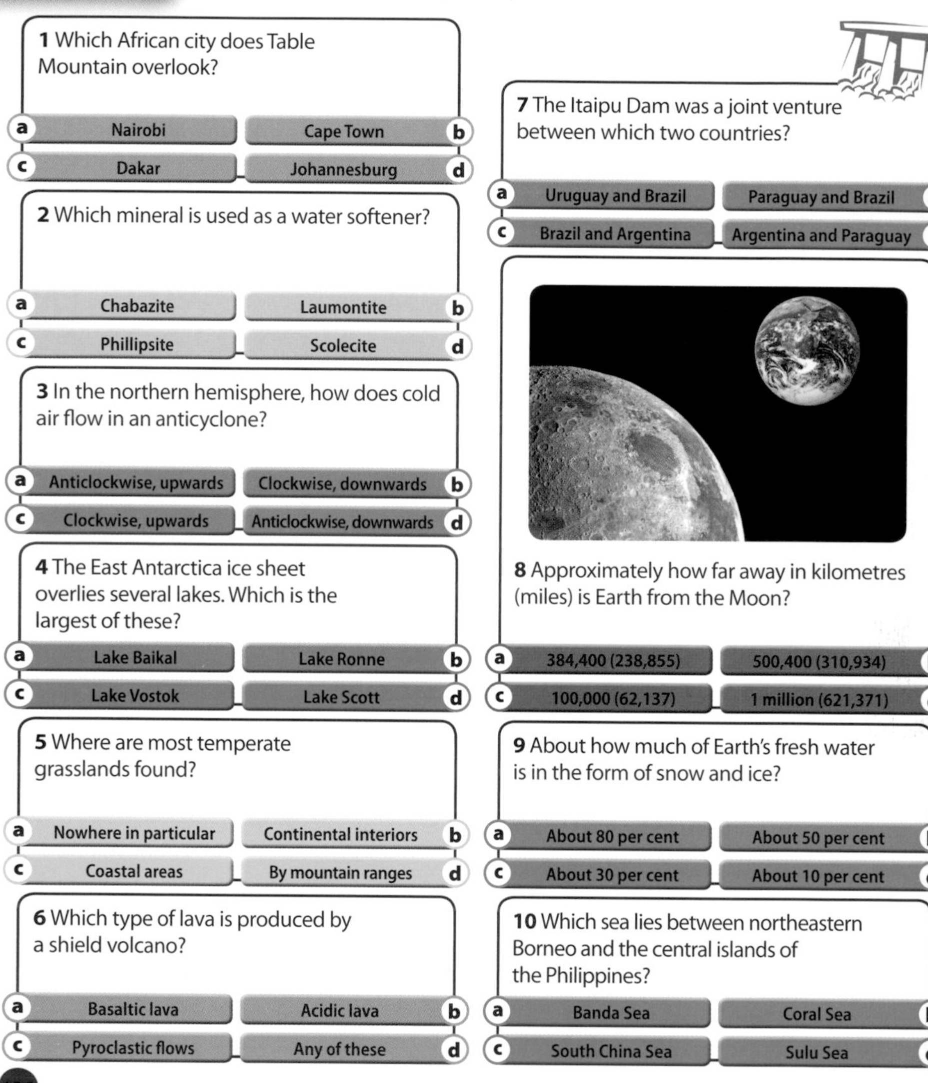

1 Which African city does Table Mountain overlook?

a Nairobi
b Cape Town
c Dakar
d Johannesburg

2 Which mineral is used as a water softener?

a Chabazite
b Laumontite
c Phillipsite
d Scolecite

3 In the northern hemisphere, how does cold air flow in an anticyclone?

a Anticlockwise, upwards
b Clockwise, downwards
c Clockwise, upwards
d Anticlockwise, downwards

4 The East Antarctica ice sheet overlies several lakes. Which is the largest of these?

a Lake Baikal
b Lake Ronne
c Lake Vostok
d Lake Scott

5 Where are most temperate grasslands found?

a Nowhere in particular
b Continental interiors
c Coastal areas
d By mountain ranges

6 Which type of lava is produced by a shield volcano?

a Basaltic lava
b Acidic lava
c Pyroclastic flows
d Any of these

7 The Itaipu Dam was a joint venture between which two countries?

a Uruguay and Brazil
b Paraguay and Brazil
c Brazil and Argentina
d Argentina and Paraguay

8 Approximately how far away in kilometres (miles) is Earth from the Moon?

a 384,400 (238,855)
b 500,400 (310,934)
c 100,000 (62,137)
d 1 million (621,371)

9 About how much of Earth's fresh water is in the form of snow and ice?

a About 80 per cent
b About 50 per cent
c About 30 per cent
d About 10 per cent

10 Which sea lies between northeastern Borneo and the central islands of the Philippines?

a Banda Sea
b Coral Sea
c South China Sea
d Sulu Sea

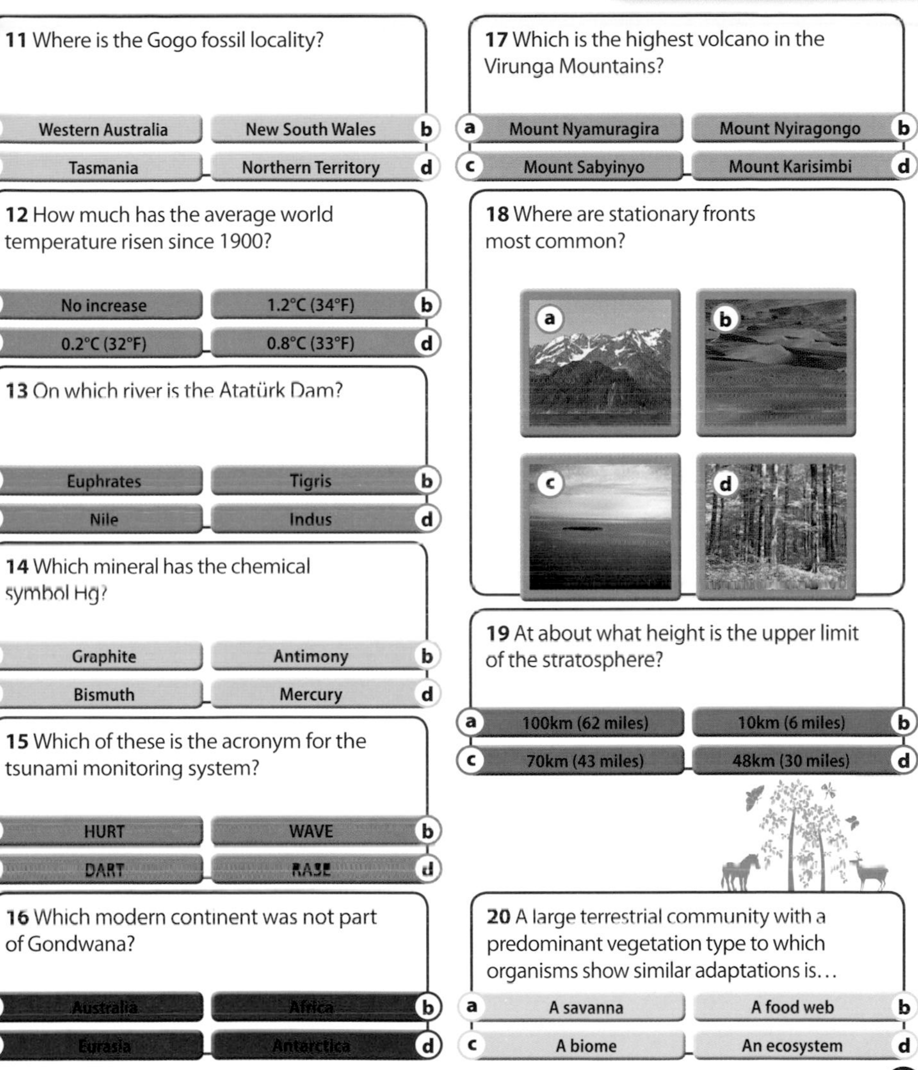

11 Where is the Gogo fossil locality?

a Western Australia
b New South Wales
c Tasmania
d Northern Territory

12 How much has the average world temperature risen since 1900?

a No increase
b 1.2°C (34°F)
c 0.2°C (32°F)
d 0.8°C (33°F)

13 On which river is the Atatürk Dam?

a Euphrates
b Tigris
c Nile
d Indus

14 Which mineral has the chemical symbol Hg?

a Graphite
b Antimony
c Bismuth
d Mercury

15 Which of these is the acronym for the tsunami monitoring system?

a HURT
b WAVE
c DART
d RASE

16 Which modern continent was not part of Gondwana?

a Australia
b Africa
c Eurasia
d Antarctica

17 Which is the highest volcano in the Virunga Mountains?

a Mount Nyamuragira
b Mount Nyiragongo
c Mount Sabyinyo
d Mount Karisimbi

18 Where are stationary fronts most common?

a
b
c
d

19 At about what height is the upper limit of the stratosphere?

a 100km (62 miles)
b 10km (6 miles)
c 70km (43 miles)
d 48km (30 miles)

20 A large terrestrial community with a predominant vegetation type to which organisms show similar adaptations is…

a A savanna
b A food web
c A biome
d An ecosystem

Quiz 52

Welwitschia **plants** in the Namib desert

1 When dripping water falls on the floor, calcite is deposited. This builds up into which structures?

- **a** Tufa
- **b** Cones
- **c** Stalagheaps
- **d** Stalagmites

2 The planet Mercury is nearest to the Sun. Where does Earth rank?

- **a** Fourth
- **b** Third
- **c** Second
- **d** Fifth

3 When did the last ice age end?

- **a** 10,000 years ago
- **b** 1 million years ago
- **c** 1 billion years ago
- **d** 1,000 years ago

4 On which continent are the Atlas mountains?

- **a** Australasia
- **b** Africa
- **c** N America
- **d** Europe

5 The Beaufort scale was first devised for use by who?

- **a** Shooting parties
- **b** Air balloonists
- **c** Gardeners
- **d** Naval officers

6 Which gas protects life on Earth from harmful ultraviolet rays?

- **a** Ozone
- **b** Carbon dioxide
- **c** Hydrogen
- **d** Xenon

can **live** for **2,500 years**

Difficulty level: **Easy**

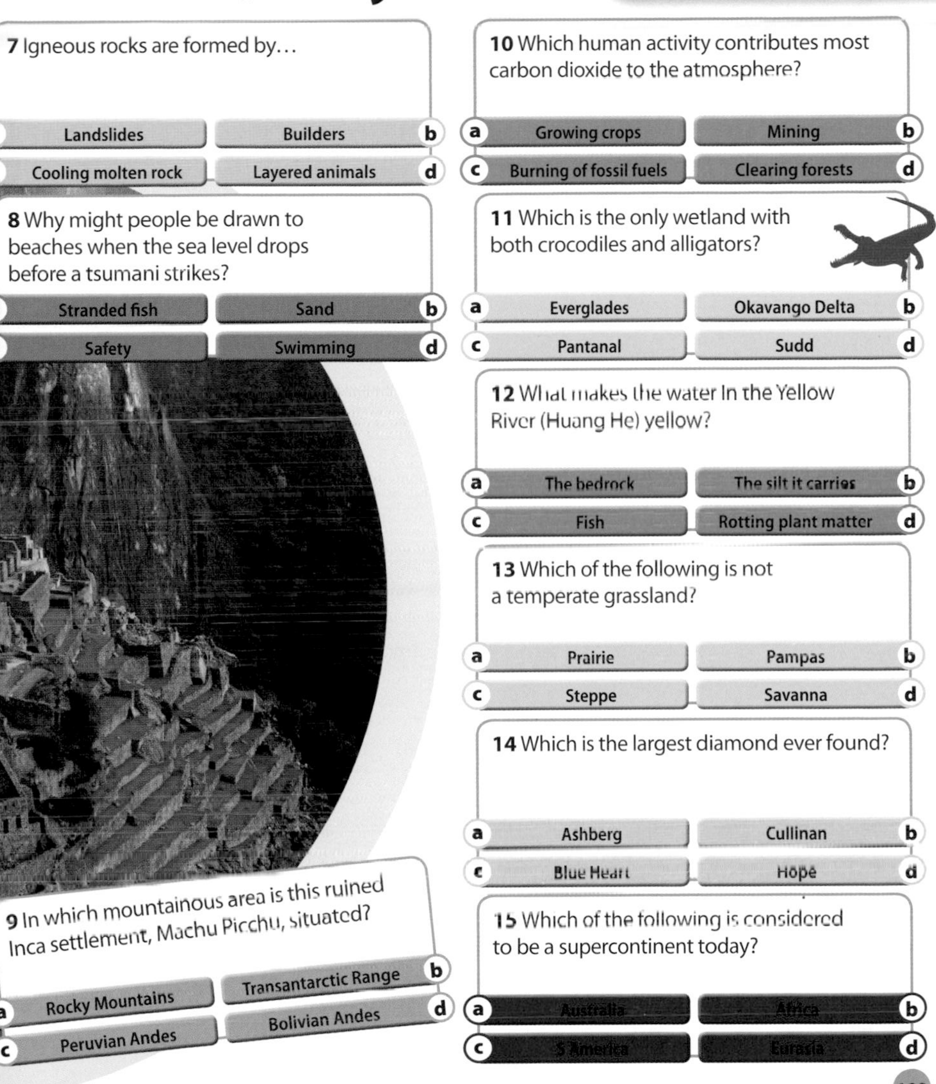

7 Igneous rocks are formed by…

a Landslides
b Builders
c Cooling molten rock
d Layered animals

8 Why might people be drawn to beaches when the sea level drops before a tsumani strikes?

a Stranded fish
b Sand
c Safety
d Swimming

9 In which mountainous area is this ruined Inca settlement, Machu Picchu, situated?

a Rocky Mountains
b Transantarctic Range
c Peruvian Andes
d Bolivian Andes

10 Which human activity contributes most carbon dioxide to the atmosphere?

a Growing crops
b Mining
c Burning of fossil fuels
d Clearing forests

11 Which is the only wetland with both crocodiles and alligators?

a Everglades
b Okavango Delta
c Pantanal
d Sudd

12 What makes the water in the Yellow River (Huang He) yellow?

a The bedrock
b The silt it carries
c Fish
d Rotting plant matter

13 Which of the following is not a temperate grassland?

a Prairie
b Pampas
c Steppe
d Savanna

14 Which is the largest diamond ever found?

a Ashberg
b Cullinan
c Blue Heart
d Hope

15 Which of the following is considered to be a supercontinent today?

a Australia
b Africa
c S America
d Eurasia

Quiz **53**

There are at least **76 active**

1 Spring and neap tides are about how much higher or lower than average?

- a About 20 per cent
- b About 50 per cent
- c About 30 per cent
- d About 70 per cent

2 Where is the largest diamond mine in the world?

- a Ontario, Canada
- b Orapa, Botswana
- c Papua, Indonesia
- d California, US

3 What is the height of the mountain K2?

- a 9,013m (29,570ft)
- b 8,611m (28,251ft)
- c 8,850m (29,035ft)
- d 6,850m (22,474ft)

4 How many capital cities does the River Danube flow through?

- a 6
- b 5
- c 4
- d 3

5 Where do most shallow focus earthquakes occur?

- a Divergence zones
- b Deep below the crust
- c Crust or just beneath it
- d Subduction zones

6 One of the largest mangrove swamps in the world is on the Bay of Bengal. What is it called?

- a Everglades
- b Marismas Nacionales
- c Sihcao Wetlands
- d Sundarbans

7 Dipterocarps from tropical lowland forests are an important source of what?

- a Timber
- b Resins
- c Essential oils
- d All of these

8 The lowest point in Australia is also the site of the country's largest lake, which fills only about twice a century. What is it called?

- a Lake Adelaide
- b Lake Eyre
- c Lake Scott
- d Lake Murray

9 Which sea is expanding due to divergence of tectonic plates?

- a Mediterranean Sea
- b Baltic Sea
- c Red Sea
- d Caribbean Sea

10 The texture of igneous rocks depends on what?

- a Rate of cooling
- b Type of magma
- c Amount of water
- d Position on slope

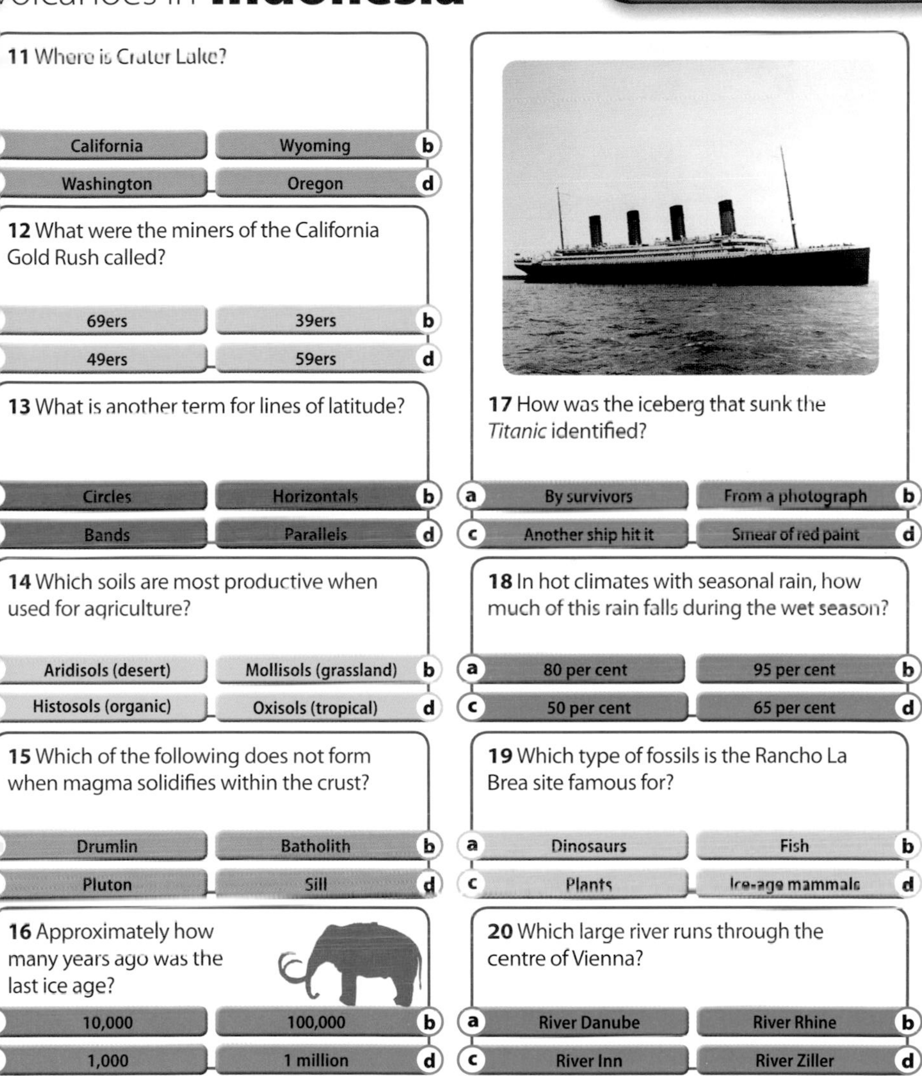

11 Where is Crater Lake?

California	Wyoming b
Washington	Oregon d

12 What were the miners of the California Gold Rush called?

69ers	39ers b
49ers	59ers d

13 What is another term for lines of latitude?

Circles	Horizontals b
Bands	Parallels d

14 Which soils are most productive when used for agriculture?

Aridisols (desert)	Mollisols (grassland) b
Histosols (organic)	Oxisols (tropical) d

15 Which of the following does not form when magma solidifies within the crust?

Drumlin	Batholith b
Pluton	Sill d

16 Approximately how many years ago was the last ice age?

10,000	100,000 b
1,000	1 million d

17 How was the iceberg that sunk the *Titanic* identified?

a By survivors	From a photograph b
c Another ship hit it	Smear of red paint d

18 In hot climates with seasonal rain, how much of this rain falls during the wet season?

a 80 per cent	95 per cent b
c 50 per cent	65 per cent d

19 Which type of fossils is the Rancho La Brea site famous for?

a Dinosaurs	Fish b
c Plants	Ice-age mammals d

20 Which large river runs through the centre of Vienna?

a River Danube	River Rhine b
c River Inn	River Ziller d

About **40 per cent** of Earth's lanc

1 What do sensors on the ocean floor measure in order to detect the passage of a tsunami wave?

a Speed
b Wavelength
c Height
d Pressure

2 With depths of 1.6km (1 mile), which is the world's deepest lake?

a Lake Balkhash
b Lake Victoria
c Lake Baikal
d Lake Superior

3 In which era did the supercontinent Laurasia exist?

a Palaeozoic
b Cenozoic
c Proterozoic
d Mesozoic

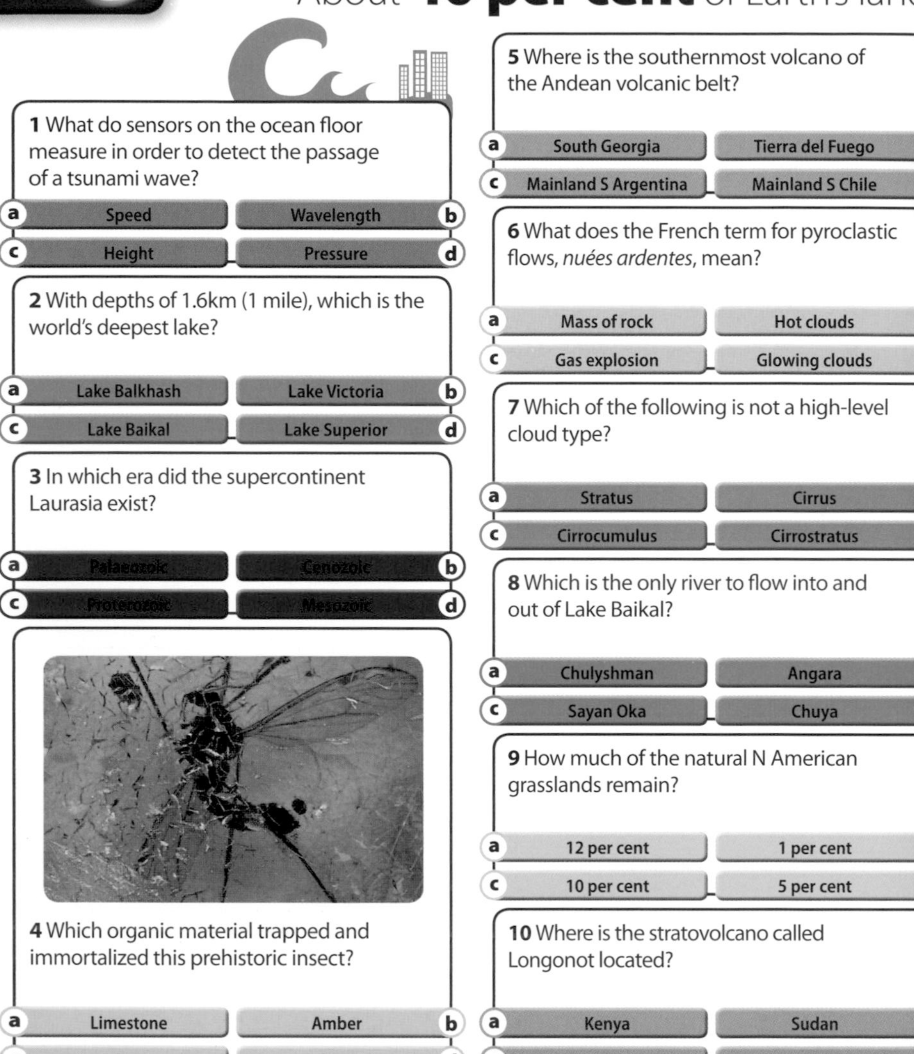

4 Which organic material trapped and immortalized this prehistoric insect?

a Limestone
b Amber
c Tar
d Peat

5 Where is the southernmost volcano of the Andean volcanic belt?

a South Georgia
b Tierra del Fuego
c Mainland S Argentina
d Mainland S Chile

6 What does the French term for pyroclastic flows, *nuées ardentes*, mean?

a Mass of rock
b Hot clouds
c Gas explosion
d Glowing clouds

7 Which of the following is not a high-level cloud type?

a Stratus
b Cirrus
c Cirrocumulus
d Cirrostratus

8 Which is the only river to flow into and out of Lake Baikal?

a Chulyshman
b Angara
c Sayan Oka
d Chuya

9 How much of the natural N American grasslands remain?

a 12 per cent
b 1 per cent
c 10 per cent
d 5 per cent

10 Where is the stratovolcano called Longonot located?

a Kenya
b Sudan
c Zimbabwe
d Malawi

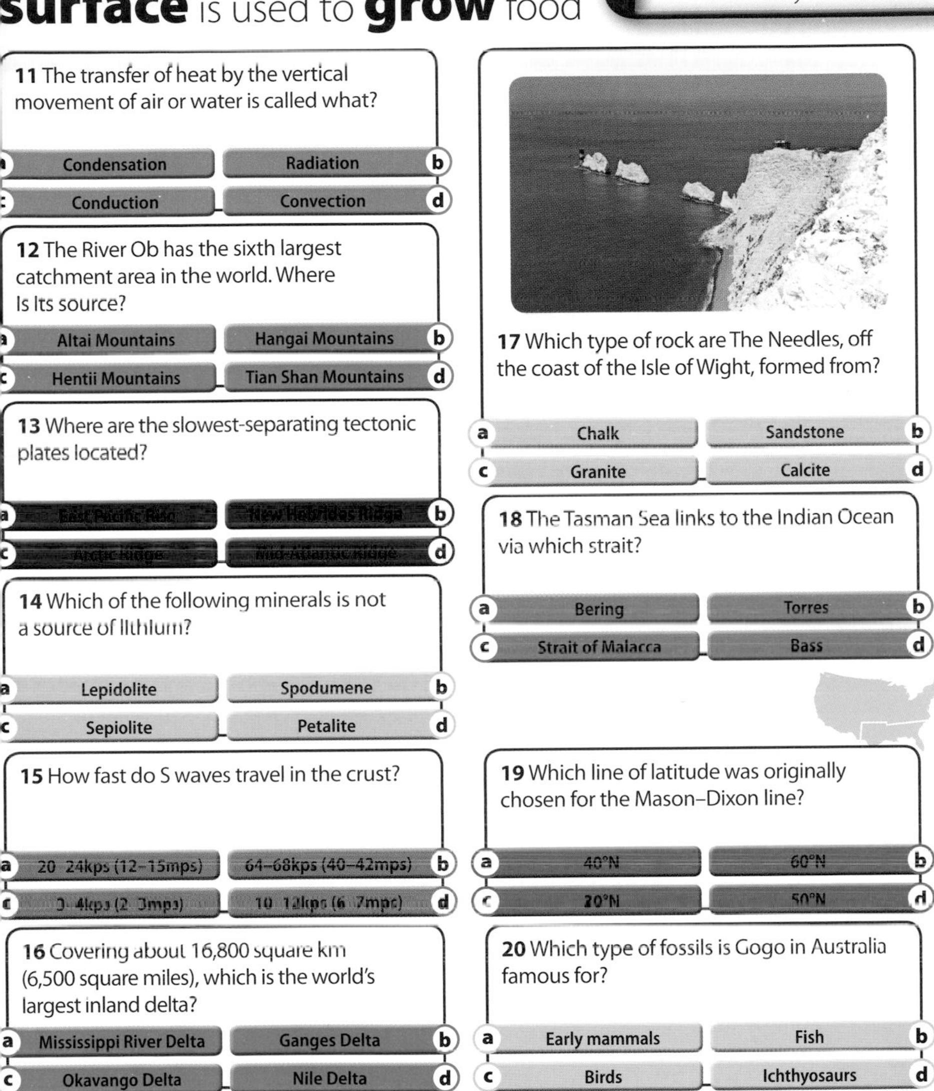

11 The transfer of heat by the vertical movement of air or water is called what?

- a Condensation
- b Radiation
- c Conduction
- d Convection

12 The River Ob has the sixth largest catchment area in the world. Where Is Its source?

- a Altai Mountains
- b Hangai Mountains
- c Hentii Mountains
- d Tian Shan Mountains

13 Where are the slowest-separating tectonic plates located?

- a East Pacific Rise
- b New Hebrides Ridge
- c Arctic Ridge
- d Mid-Atlantic Ridge

14 Which of the following minerals is not a source of lithium?

- a Lepidolite
- b Spodumene
- c Sepiolite
- d Petalite

15 How fast do S waves travel in the crust?

- a 20–24kps (12–15mps)
- b 64–68kps (40–42mps)
- c 3–4kps (2–3mps)
- d 10–12kps (6–7mps)

16 Covering about 16,800 square km (6,500 square miles), which is the world's largest inland delta?

- a Mississippi River Delta
- b Ganges Delta
- c Okavango Delta
- d Nile Delta

17 Which type of rock are The Needles, off the coast of the Isle of Wight, formed from?

- a Chalk
- b Sandstone
- c Granite
- d Calcite

18 The Tasman Sea links to the Indian Ocean via which strait?

- a Bering
- b Torres
- c Strait of Malacca
- d Bass

19 Which line of latitude was originally chosen for the Mason–Dixon line?

- a 40°N
- b 60°N
- c 30°N
- d 50°N

20 Which type of fossils is Gogo in Australia famous for?

- a Early mammals
- b Fish
- c Birds
- d Ichthyosaurs

Quiz 55

About **30 per cent** of Earth's total

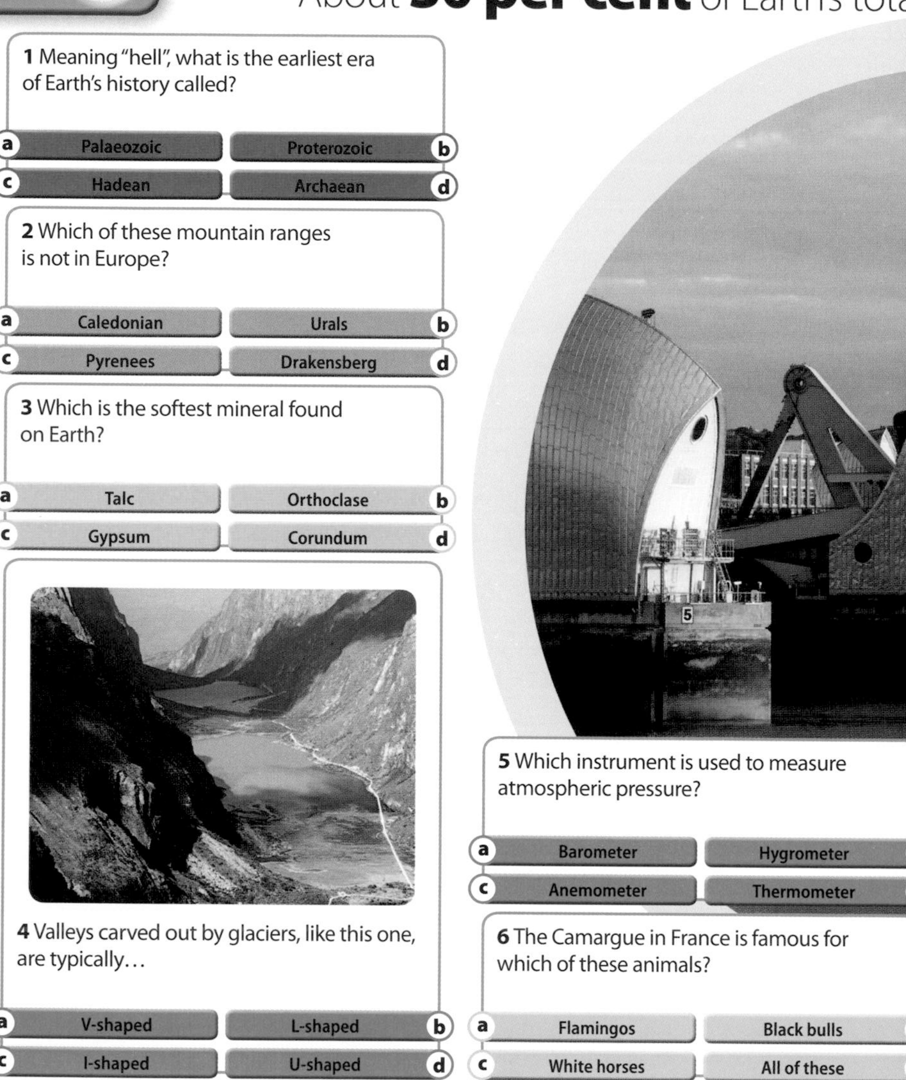

1 Meaning "hell", what is the earliest era of Earth's history called?

a Palaeozoic
b Proterozoic
c Hadean
d Archaean

2 Which of these mountain ranges is not in Europe?

a Caledonian
b Urals
c Pyrenees
d Drakensberg

3 Which is the softest mineral found on Earth?

a Talc
b Orthoclase
c Gypsum
d Corundum

4 Valleys carved out by glaciers, like this one, are typically…

a V-shaped
b L-shaped
c I-shaped
d U-shaped

5 Which instrument is used to measure atmospheric pressure?

a Barometer
b Hygrometer
c Anemometer
d Thermometer

6 The Camargue in France is famous for which of these animals?

a Flamingos
b Black bulls
c White horses
d All of these

7 What is the purpose of this structure on the Thames in England?

- a Housing
- b Storing ships
- c Flood control
- d Generating electricity

8 How might we know today of a tsunami in the historical past?

- a Geological evidence
- b Historical documents
- c Folklore and legend
- d All of these

9 In 1983 what was found in the ozone layer over the South Pole?

- a Pollutants
- b A hole
- c A thicker area
- d Nothing human-related

10 Ngorongoro Crater is in which tropical grassland national park?

- a Serengeti
- b Masai Mara
- c Nairobi
- d Tsavo East

11 Why does gold have important industrial applications?

- a High conductivity
- b Non-reactive
- c Easily workable
- d All of these

12 Measured from base to peak, which is the world's tallest mountain?

- a K2
- b Mount Aconcagua
- c Mauna Kea
- d Mount Everest

13 Why do people in Luxor and Aswan not need umbrellas?

- a They like getting wet
- b There is so little rain
- c They use hats
- d They stay indoors

14 What do you call a person who studies fossils?

- a Archaeologist
- b Osteologist
- c Palaeontologist
- d Fossil hunter

15 What are small tectonic plates called?

- a Microplates
- b Miniplates
- c Plate chips
- d Microchips

Quiz 56

The **Namib Desert** is one of the

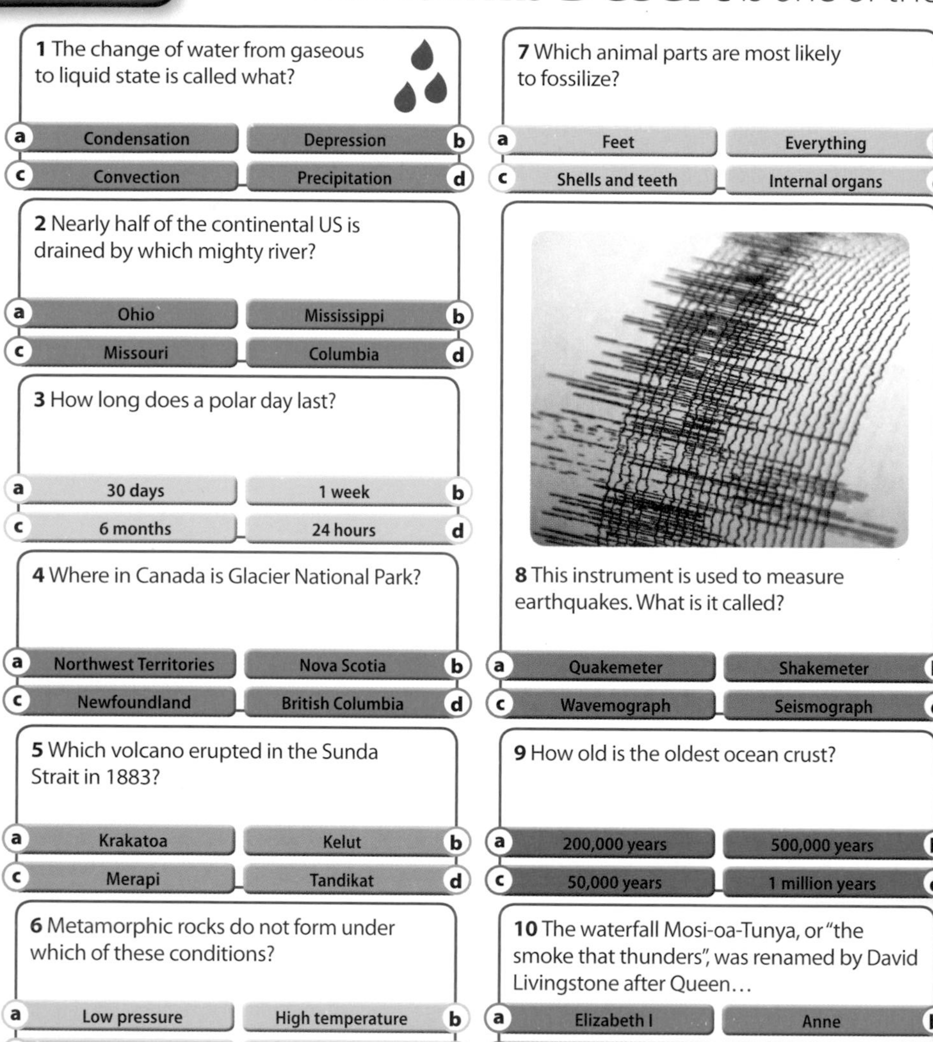

1 The change of water from gaseous to liquid state is called what?

a Condensation
b Depression
c Convection
d Precipitation

2 Nearly half of the continental US is drained by which mighty river?

a Ohio
b Mississippi
c Missouri
d Columbia

3 How long does a polar day last?

a 30 days
b 1 week
c 6 months
d 24 hours

4 Where in Canada is Glacier National Park?

a Northwest Territories
b Nova Scotia
c Newfoundland
d British Columbia

5 Which volcano erupted in the Sunda Strait in 1883?

a Krakatoa
b Kelut
c Merapi
d Tandikat

6 Metamorphic rocks do not form under which of these conditions?

a Low pressure
b High temperature
c High pressure
d Heat and high pressure

7 Which animal parts are most likely to fossilize?

a Feet
b Everything
c Shells and teeth
d Internal organs

8 This instrument is used to measure earthquakes. What is it called?

a Quakemeter
b Shakemeter
c Wavemograph
d Seismograph

9 How old is the oldest ocean crust?

a 200,000 years
b 500,000 years
c 50,000 years
d 1 million years

10 The waterfall Mosi-oa-Tunya, or "the smoke that thunders", was renamed by David Livingstone after Queen…

a Elizabeth I
b Anne
c Victoria
d Elizabeth II

11 At which depth, on average, are hydrothermal vents found?

- a 5,300m (17,388ft)
- b 10,400m (34,121ft)
- c 200m (656ft)
- d 2,100m (6,890ft)

12 Hot, dry climates are found where?

- a In polar regions
- b At mid-latitudes
- c In the tropics
- d At high altitude

13 Which volcanic rock forms when lava cools too quickly for crystals to grow?

- a Andesite
- b Tephra
- c Obsidian
- d Pumice

14 Where is the fossil locality called the Jurassic Coast?

- a East coast of Canada
- b West coast of US
- c North coast of Africa
- d South coast of England

15 Which is the largest lake in Europe?

- a Ladoga
- b Geneva
- c Lough Derg
- d Como

16 In which desert landscape did John Ford film many of his westerns, including *Stagecoach*?

- a San Fernando Valley
- b Monument Valley
- c Death Valley
- d Yosemite

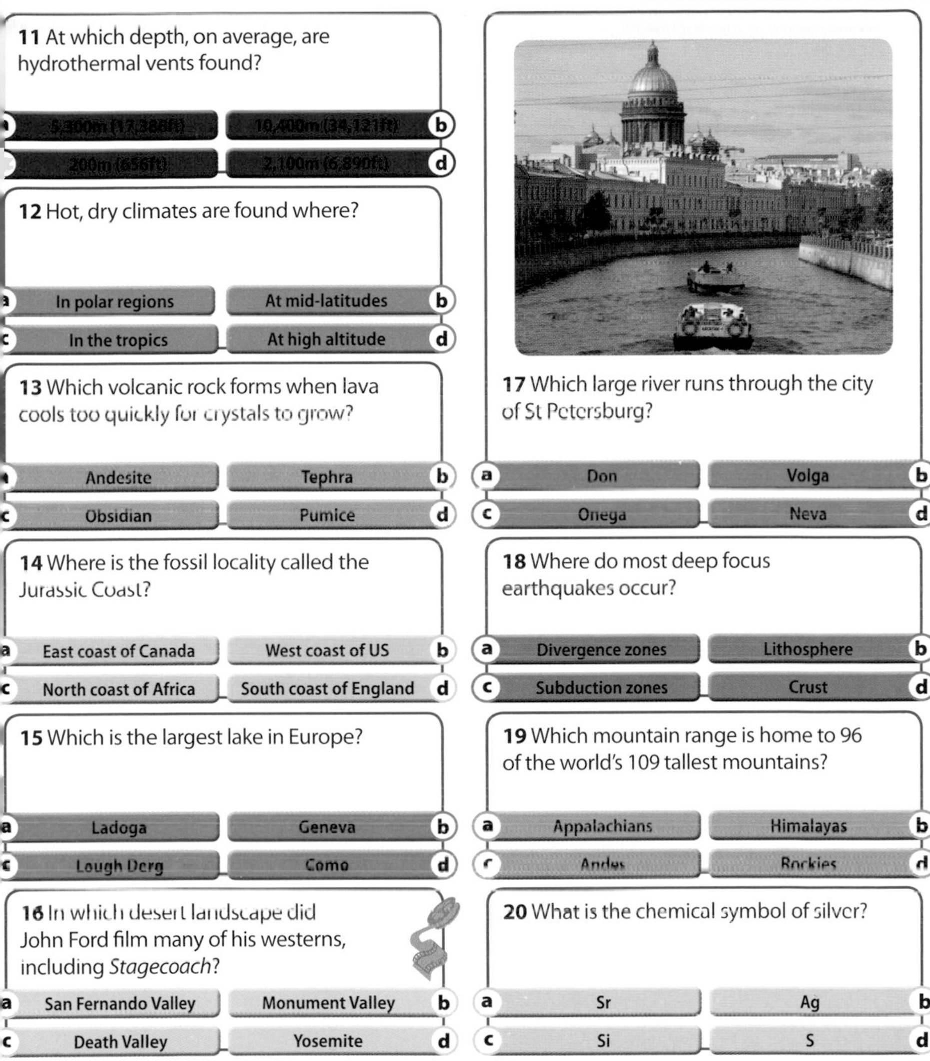

17 Which large river runs through the city of St Petersburg?

- a Don
- b Volga
- c Onega
- d Neva

18 Where do most deep focus earthquakes occur?

- a Divergence zones
- b Lithosphere
- c Subduction zones
- d Crust

19 Which mountain range is home to 96 of the world's 109 tallest mountains?

- a Appalachians
- b Himalayas
- c Andes
- d Rockies

20 What is the chemical symbol of silver?

- a Sr
- b Ag
- c Si
- d S

The **Nile** winds its way through

1 When did the Kobe earthquake occur?

- a 1995
- b 1950
- c 1890
- d 2006

2 Which of the following is the state fossil of Alaska?

- a *Mammuthus*
- b *Smilodon*
- c *Megalonyx*
- d *Mastodon*

3 Which is the highest navigable lake in the world?

- a Lake Baikal
- b Ozero Issyk-Kul'
- c Qinghai Hu
- d Lake Titicaca

4 In which era did the supercontinent Rodinia exist?

- a Palaeozoic
- b Cenozoic
- c Mesozoic
- d Proterozoic

5 What is a visible electrical discharge within a cloud called?

- a Thunderbolt
- b Sheet lightning
- c Fork lightning
- d Lightning flash

6 Which of these countries has the lowest biodiversity?

- a Ecuador
- b Germany
- c Australia
- d India

7 Which type of lake is Loch Ness?

- a Piedmont
- b Fault
- c Kettle
- d Crater

8 Which type of cloud are cold fronts usually associated with?

- a Stratus
- b Altostratus
- c Cumulus
- d Cirrus

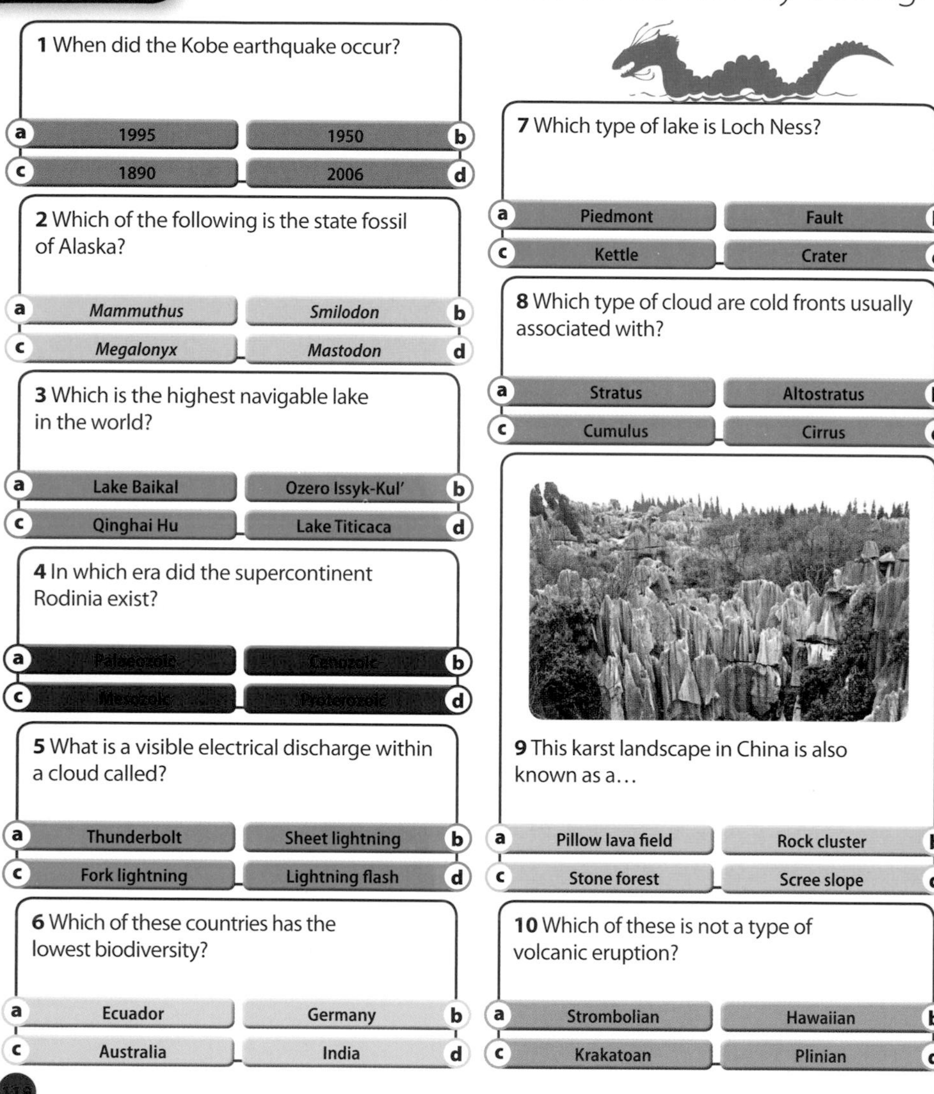

9 This karst landscape in China is also known as a…

- a Pillow lava field
- b Rock cluster
- c Stone forest
- d Scree slope

10 Which of these is not a type of volcanic eruption?

- a Strombolian
- b Hawaiian
- c Krakatoan
- d Plinian

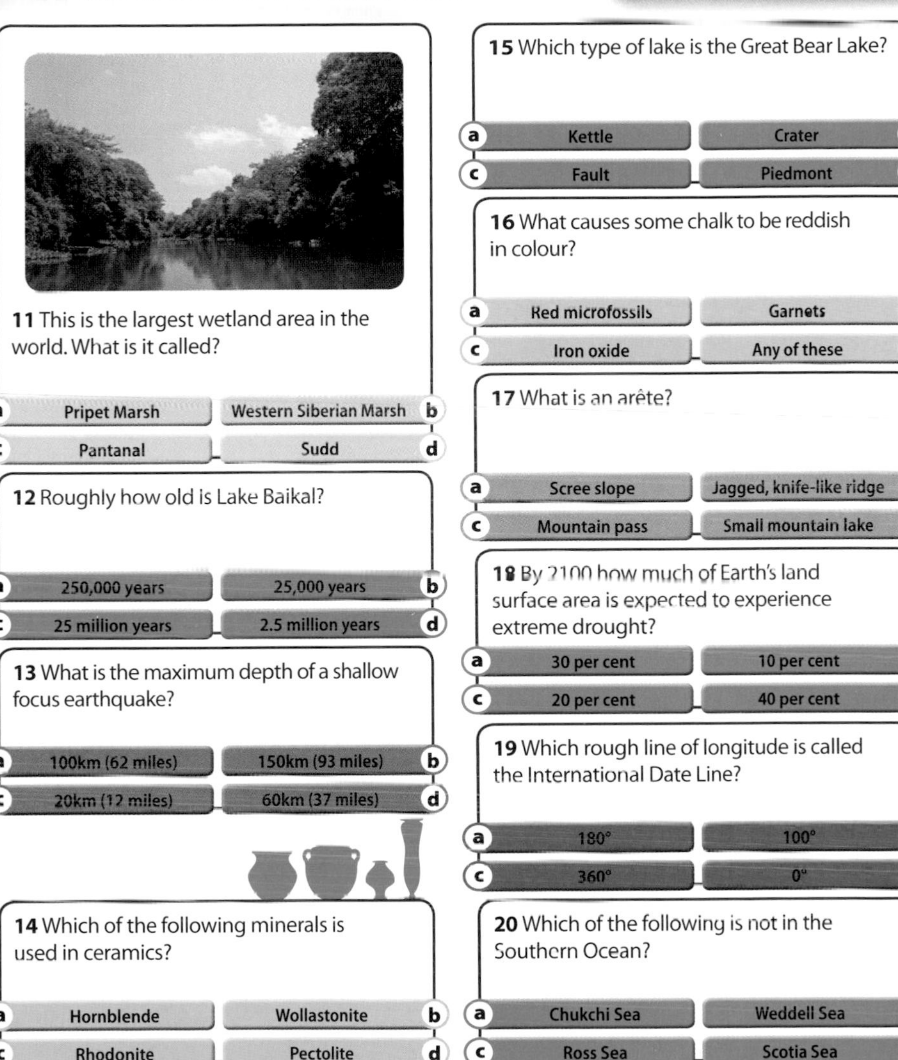

11 This is the largest wetland area in the world. What is it called?

- a Pripet Marsh
- b Western Siberian Marsh
- c Pantanal
- d Sudd

12 Roughly how old is Lake Baikal?

- a 250,000 years
- b 25,000 years
- c 25 million years
- d 2.5 million years

13 What is the maximum depth of a shallow focus earthquake?

- a 100km (62 miles)
- b 150km (93 miles)
- c 20km (12 miles)
- d 60km (37 miles)

14 Which of the following minerals is used in ceramics?

- a Hornblende
- b Wollastonite
- c Rhodonite
- d Pectolite

15 Which type of lake is the Great Bear Lake?

- a Kettle
- b Crater
- c Fault
- d Piedmont

16 What causes some chalk to be reddish in colour?

- a Red microfossils
- b Garnets
- c Iron oxide
- d Any of these

17 What is an arête?

- a Scree slope
- b Jagged, knife-like ridge
- c Mountain pass
- d Small mountain lake

18 By 2100 how much of Earth's land surface area is expected to experience extreme drought?

- a 30 per cent
- b 10 per cent
- c 20 per cent
- d 40 per cent

19 Which rough line of longitude is called the International Date Line?

- a 180°
- b 100°
- c 360°
- d 0°

20 Which of the following is not in the Southern Ocean?

- a Chukchi Sea
- b Weddell Sea
- c Ross Sea
- d Scotia Sea

Quiz **58**

About **6,000** lightning **flashes**

1 Which of these mammals is considered essential to the wellbeing of the rainforests in Java and Sumatra?

a 

b 

c 

d 

2 Who sang "Singin' in the Rain" in the 1952 film of the same name?

a Gene Kelly
b Fred Astaire
c Frank Sinatra
d Sammy Davis Jr

3 What was created when Earth was struck by a planet-sized object 4.5 billion years ago?

a Saturn
b A galaxy
c North Star
d The Moon

4 In technical terms volcanoes can be active, extinct, or…

a Inactive
b Dead
c Dormant
d Sleeping

5 Which of the following is not a line of latitude?

a Equator
b Tropic of Capricorn
c Prime Meridian
d Tropic of Cancer

6 In which desert is the largest copper mine in the world located?

a Sechura
b Atacama
c Patagonian
d Chihuahuan

7 Which is the longest river in the UK?

a Thames
b Ouse
c Dee
d Severn

8 Gold is ductile. What does this mean?

a Shatters easily
b Found in water
c Difficult to work with
d Easily shaped

9 How many people were killed in the Indian Ocean tsunami of 2004?

a About 1.3 million
b About 280,000
c About 560,000
d About 850

10 On which line of latitude is the Equator?

a 66° 33′ 44″ S
b 0° latitude
c 23° 26′ 16″ S
d 23° 26′ 16″ N

occur worldwide each **minute**

11 In which of the following would you not find fossils?

a Rock
b Ice
c Mud
d Resin

12 What is this mountain called?

a Mont Blanc
b Ben Nevis
c Mount Fuji
d The Matterhorn

13 How many major tectonic plates are there?

a 7
b 4
c 10
d 19

14 On 21 June, the South Pole receives how many hours of continuous darkness?

a 8
b 24
c 12
d 16

15 What type of rock is granite?

a Intrusive igneous
b Metamorphic
c Sedimentary
d Extrusive igneous

The odds of being struck by **lightning**

1 Which is the most common intrusive igneous rock?

a Basalt
b Diorite
c Pegmatite
d Granite

2 Where is Mount McKinley?

a California
b Alaska
c British Columbia
d Oregon

3 In Australia, the border of the Northern Territory and which other state lies along latitude 26°S?

a New South Wales
b Queensland
c Victoria
d South Australia

4 Where would you find the Agulhas current?

a Off S Africa
b Off S America
c Off South Australia
d Off southern India

5 To which river does the 1927 song "Ol' Man River" refer?

a Hudson
b Delaware
c Mississippi
d Missouri

6 How old is the oldest continental crust?

a 4 billion years
b 1 billion years
c 500,000 years
d 10 billion years

7 Which of the following features is not left behind by a melting glacier?

a Esker
b Kettle lake
c Drumlin
d V-shaped valley

8 Which of the following is not a seismic wave?

a Rayleigh wave
b Love wave
c Drake wave
d P wave

9 On which river does Lisbon lie?

a Tagus
b Ebro
c Douro
d Alcoa

10 What do you call gemstones with a rounded upper surface and flat underside?

a Carbochons
b Cushions
c Baguettes
d Step-cut

in your **lifetime** are 3,000 to 1

Difficulty level: **Medium**

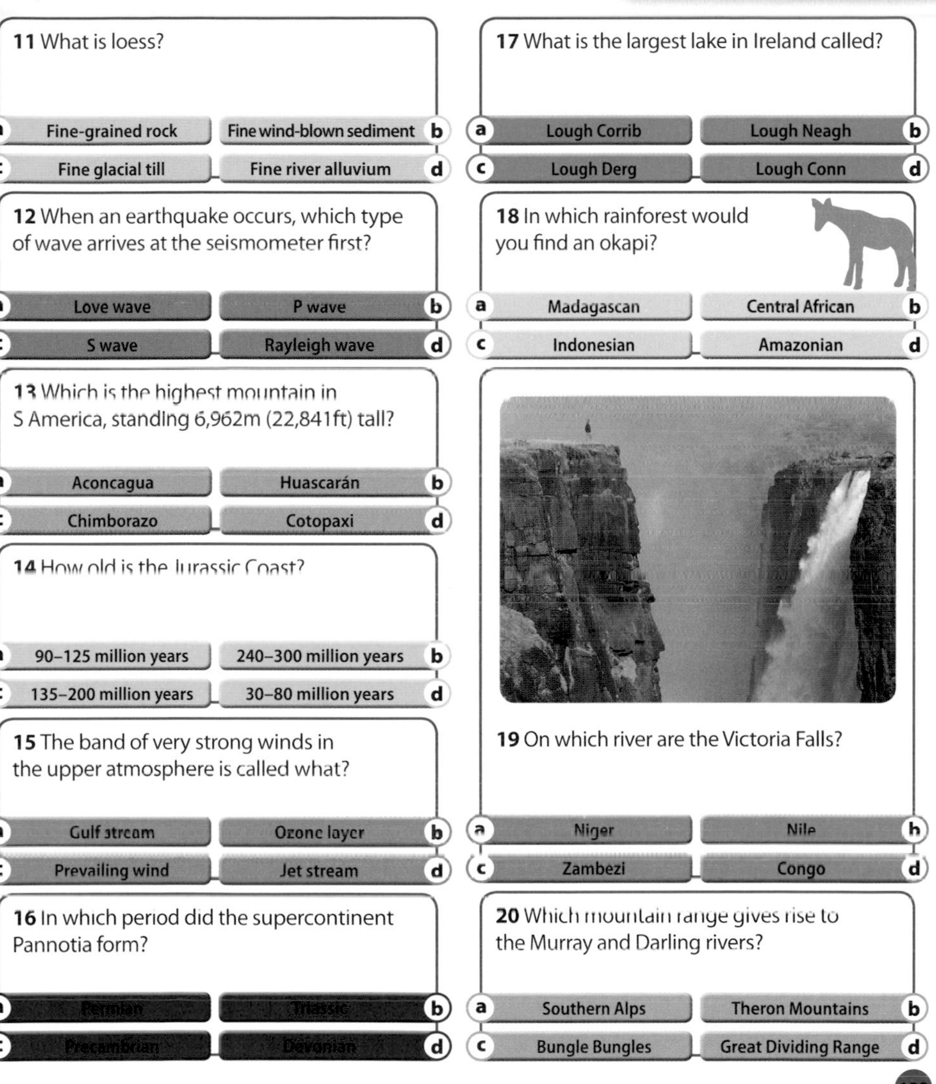

11 What is loess?

a Fine-grained rock
b Fine wind-blown sediment
c Fine glacial till
d Fine river alluvium

12 When an earthquake occurs, which type of wave arrives at the seismometer first?

a Love wave
b P wave
c S wave
d Rayleigh wave

13 Which is the highest mountain in S America, standing 6,962m (22,841ft) tall?

a Aconcagua
b Huascarán
c Chimborazo
d Cotopaxi

14 How old is the Jurassic Coast?

a 90–125 million years
b 240–300 million years
c 135–200 million years
d 30–80 million years

15 The band of very strong winds in the upper atmosphere is called what?

a Gulf stream
b Ozone layer
c Prevailing wind
d Jet stream

16 In which period did the supercontinent Pannotia form?

a Permian
b Triassic
c Precambrian
d Devonian

17 What is the largest lake in Ireland called?

a Lough Corrib
b Lough Neagh
c Lough Derg
d Lough Conn

18 In which rainforest would you find an okapi?

a Madagascan
b Central African
c Indonesian
d Amazonian

19 On which river are the Victoria Falls?

a Niger
b Nile
c Zambezi
d Congo

20 Which mountain range gives rise to the Murray and Darling rivers?

a Southern Alps
b Theron Mountains
c Bungle Bungles
d Great Dividing Range

Cotopaxi, in the Andes, is the world's

1 Which is the deepest lake in England's Lake District?

- a Windermere
- b Coniston
- c Grasmere
- d Wastwater

2 How many people died in Japan in the Great Kantō earthquake of 1923?

- a About 50,000
- b About 6,000
- c About 1 million
- d About 140,000

3 When was the Beaufort wind scale devised?

- a 1915
- b 1940
- c 1805
- d 1875

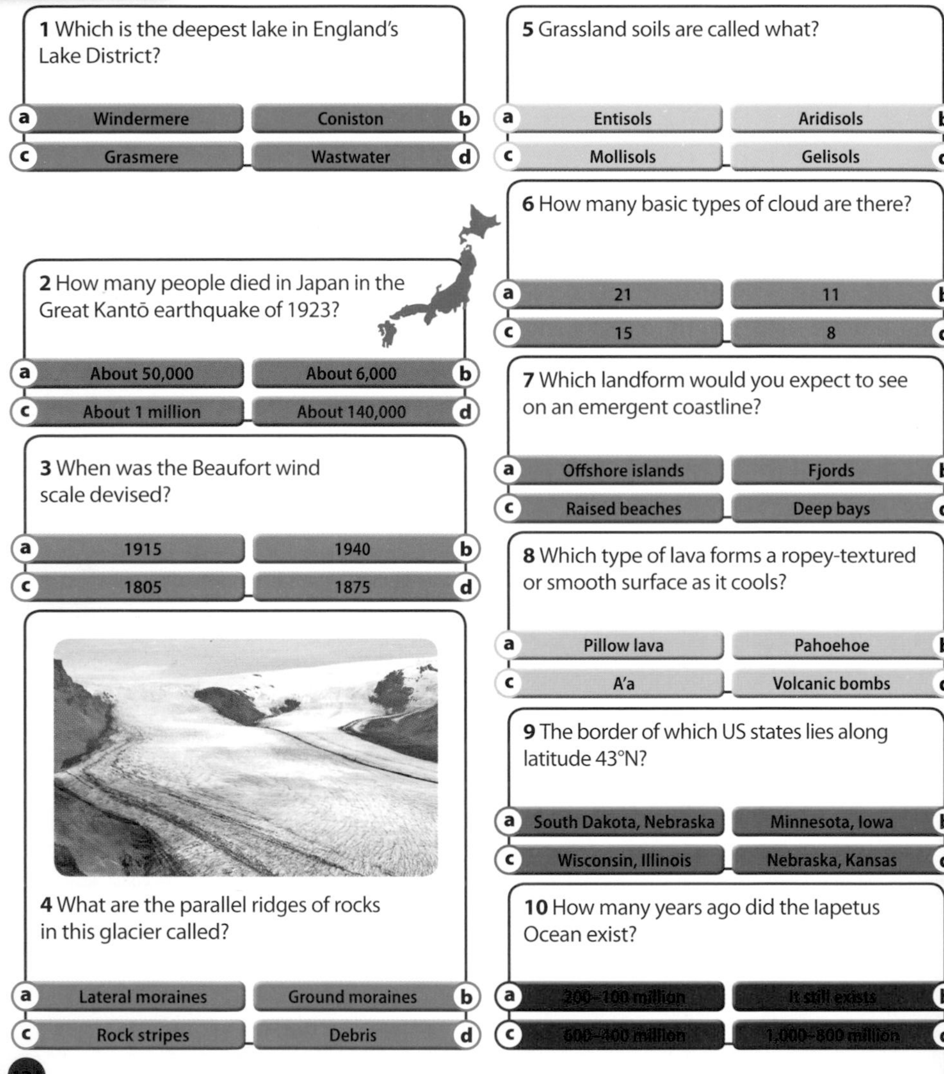

4 What are the parallel ridges of rocks in this glacier called?

- a Lateral moraines
- b Ground moraines
- c Rock stripes
- d Debris

5 Grassland soils are called what?

- a Entisols
- b Aridisols
- c Mollisols
- d Gelisols

6 How many basic types of cloud are there?

- a 21
- b 11
- c 15
- d 8

7 Which landform would you expect to see on an emergent coastline?

- a Offshore islands
- b Fjords
- c Raised beaches
- d Deep bays

8 Which type of lava forms a ropey-textured or smooth surface as it cools?

- a Pillow lava
- b Pahoehoe
- c A'a
- d Volcanic bombs

9 The border of which US states lies along latitude 43°N?

- a South Dakota, Nebraska
- b Minnesota, Iowa
- c Wisconsin, Illinois
- d Nebraska, Kansas

10 How many years ago did the Iapetus Ocean exist?

- a 300–100 million
- b It still exists
- c 600–400 million
- d 1,000–800 million

highest active volcano

Difficulty level: **Hard**

11 Instead of flowing into the sea, which river ends in the desert, forming the world's largest inland delta?

a Congo
b Okavango
c Orange
d Zambezi

12 A good index fossil should be widespread and...

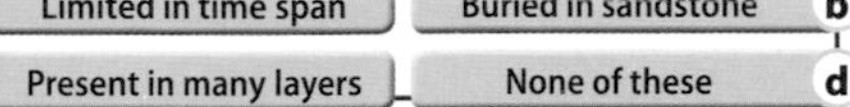

a Limited in time span
b Buried in sandstone
c Present in many layers
d None of these

13 The science of the shape and size of Earth is called what?

a Geography
b Geodesy
c Geology
d Geomorphology

14 What is a tropical cyclone in the Pacific Ocean called?

a Typhoon
b Hurricane
c Tornado
d Pacific storm

15 Which of the following is not a type of granite?

a Coarse
b Pink
c Orbicular
d Porphyritic

16 Which of these volcanoes has Plinian eruptions?

a Mount St Helens
b Stromboli
c Mauna Loa
d Surtsey

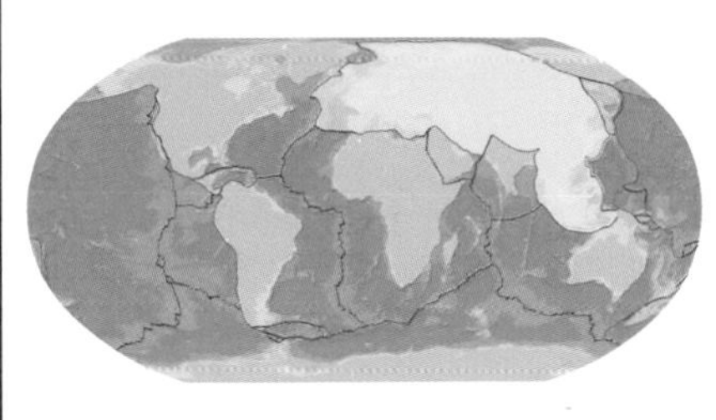

17 Which tectonic plate is highlighted here?

a African
b Pacific
c Antarctic
d Eurasian

18 How fast do S waves travel in the mantle?

a 16–21kps (10–13mps)
b 27–31kps (17–19mps)
c 4.5–7kps (3–4mps)
d 1–2kps (0.6–1.2mps)

19 Coniferous forests in cool, wet regions generally grow on which type of soil?

a Histosols
b Podzols
c Entisols
d Vertisols

20 Through which capital city does the River Vltava flow?

a Istanbul
b Budapest
c Moscow
d Prague

Planet Earth

Our planet is just like countless others in space, except for a combination of lucky accidents that make it an ideal home for life. Like all planets it orbits or travels around a star – the Sun – which generates vast amounts of energy in the form of heat and light. This energy drives Earth's weather, creates its climates, and fuels the processes of life itself.

Earth in space

Compared to the Sun, Earth is a tiny, rocky ball. It is one of the four rocky planets orbiting the Sun (but not as close as shown here). Beyond the rocky planets – Mercury, Venus, Earth, and Mars – lie four giant planets made of gas and ice: Jupiter, Saturn, Uranus, and Neptune. Only Earth and possibly Mars lie at the right distance from the Sun to support life. Mercury and Venus are too close and too hot, and the others are too cold.

Planet formation

All the planets formed from a cloud of gas, dust, and rock surrounding the Sun 4.6 billion years ago. Colliding rocks generated intense heat that welded them together into bigger masses. The bigger they grew, the more gravity they had, so they attracted more rock and kept on growing.

Earth and the Moon

Soon after Earth formed it collided with a smaller planet, smashing it into a cloud of drifting fragments. These clumped together to form the Moon. Impact craters on the Moon show where some of the final fragments crashed onto its surface.

Core, mantle, and crust

As Earth grew bigger, the energy of all the rock crashing into it turned to heat, melting the entire planet. Most of the heavy metal in the molten rock sank to the centre to form the metallic core, surrounded by the deep, rocky mantle and cool crust.

Molten core has a solid centre

Deep, very hot mantle is solid but pliable, like toffee

Shallow crust is cool and brittle

Blue planet

Water is common in space, but mostly in the form of ice or gas. Earth is just the right temperature to have oceans of liquid water. Some of it forms clouds that drift over land and bring rain. Without this water, there would be no life.

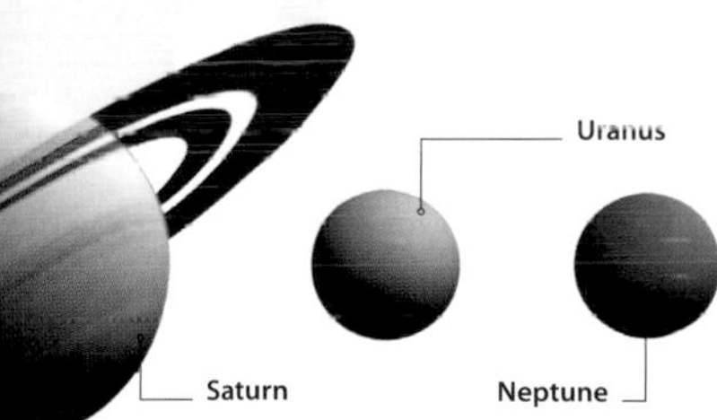

Atmosphere

The blue glow in this view of the Moon from Earth's orbit is the thin layer of gas that forms Earth's atmosphere. It is the air we breathe, but it is also vital insulation. Without it we would fry by day and freeze at night.

Plate tectonics

Planet Earth is a giant ball of hot rock, with a thin, cool, brittle crust. Nuclear energy deep inside the planet generates heat that flows up towards the surface. The heat flow sets up currents in the hot, softened mantle rock below the crust, so the crust is always moving. This has cracked it into huge plates that are also moving, reshaping the global map.

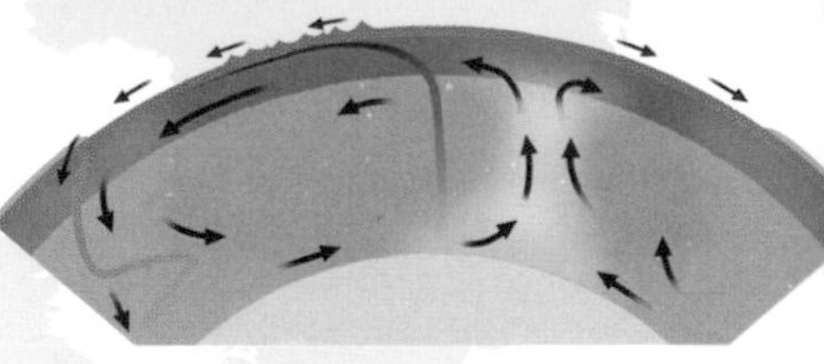

Creeping crust

Heat currents rising through the mantle flow sideways below the crust, dragging it with them. In some places they pull it apart, creating spreading rifts. In other places they drive plates of crust together, so they overlap and one is forced beneath another.

Spreading rifts

The hot mantle below the crust is kept solid by intense pressure. Where plates of the crust pull apart it eases the pressure, so the rock below melts and erupts through volcanoes along the rift. Most of these rifts lie on the ocean floors where they form mid-oceanic ridges – but this row of rift volcanoes is on Iceland.

Expanding oceans

As rifts in the ocean floor pull apart, erupting molten rock hardens to form new ocean floor. This means that some oceans such as the Atlantic are expanding. Rifts may also form new seas like the Red Sea, seen here from space.

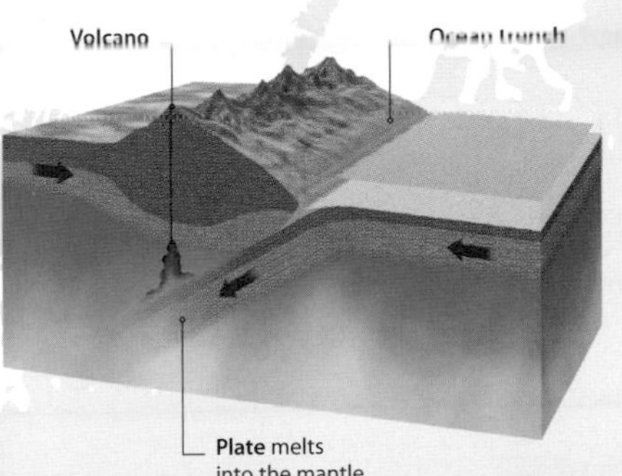

Overlapping plates

Ocean floor expansion at spreading rifts is balanced by the destruction of ocean floor at other plate boundaries, marked by deep ocean trenches. One plate of oceanic crust is driven beneath another plate, so it melts into the mantle and fuels lines of volcanoes. The plate movement may also push up ridges of high mountains.

Sliding faults

At some plate boundaries one plate of Earth's crust just slides past another, without pulling away or pushing beneath it. There are no volcanoes on the boundary, but the movement causes regular earthquakes. It can also ruck up the landscape into mountains like these lining the San Andreas Fault in California.

Building continents

Where plates overlap and one is forced beneath another, volcanoes erupt a type of lava that cools to form relatively lightweight rocks. These form slabs of thick crust that float on the mantle like huge rocky rafts. Over hundreds of millions of years these have built up to form continents.

Continental drift

As the plates pull apart, push together, or slide past each other, they carry the continents with them. This means that they are being constantly rearranged. Some 300 million years ago all Earth's landmasses came together to form a vast supercontinent known as Pangaea.

Earthquakes and tsunamis

Major earthquakes are among the most destructive natural disasters. They shake cities to the ground, and trigger tsunamis that result in catastrophic flooding. They are caused by the relentless movement of Earth's tectonic plates building up years of stress that is all released in a few seconds.

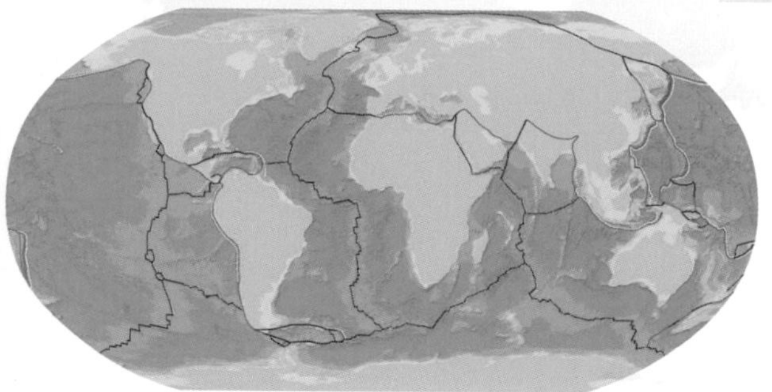

Catastrophe

Earthquakes strike without warning. The ground literally shakes, rocking buildings from side to side until they collapse. Cracks often open up in the ground, rupturing gas pipes and causing fires – and since the water pipes often break too there is no water to put the fires out.

Grinding plates

Nearly all earthquakes occur in regions where the plates of Earth's crust are either pushing together or sliding past each other. These earthquake zones are shown in green on this map of the major plate boundaries.

Creep and snap

Where the plates creep steadily past each other, the movement causes only minor damage, like this cracked road. But if they lock together, tension builds up until something snaps, triggering an earthquake.

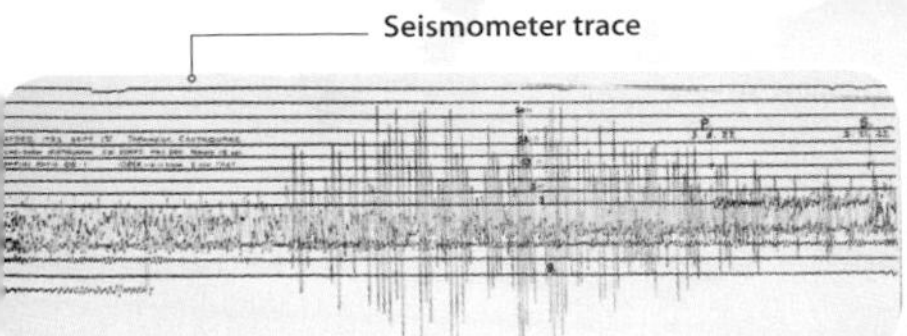

Ripple effect

The focus of an earthquake is usually deep underground, where the rocks on each side of a plate boundary suddenly shift. Shock waves ripple outwards, shaking both the ground and the seismometers that measure earthquakes.

Tsunami

If a stressed plate boundary on the ocean floor snaps – as they often do – the sudden movement of the rock pushes up a huge heap of water. This races over the ocean as broad waves that get much steeper as they approach the shore, surging inland to cause massive destruction.

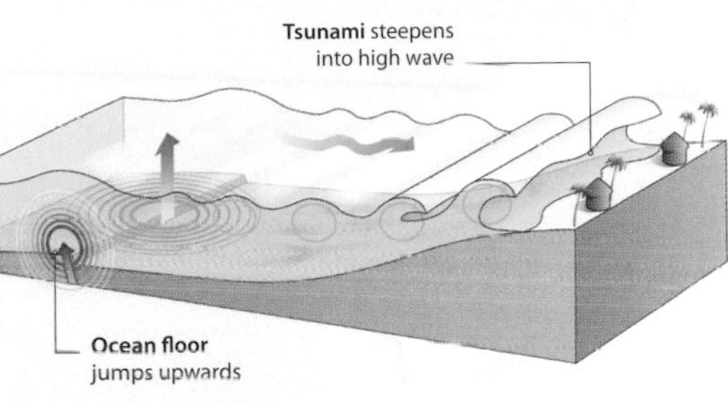

Searching the rubble

Serious earthquakes can kill thousands of people in a few minutes. Most of the victims are buried beneath collapsed buildings, as here, where a rescue worker tries to locate survivors using a sniffer dog. Tsunamis are even more deadly, drowning whole cities.

Mountains and volcanoes

The titanic forces that cause earthquakes also raise mountains and volcanoes. Most mountain ranges are huge crumple zones, created as the rocks of Earth's crust buckle under pressure from tectonic plate movement. Meanwhile physical and chemical changes deep below the surface melt the rocks and fuel volcanic eruptions.

Mountain ranges

Fold mountains mark the boundaries between colliding plates. These are the Andes, pushed up by the Pacific Ocean floor ploughing under South America. Similarly, the collision of India and Asia has raised the Himalayas.

Granite giants

Vast masses of molten rock formed deep within the crust slowly solidify into hard granite. Over time the softer rocks above and around these may be worn away. This exposes the granite, creating mountains that tower above the landscape, like Half Dome in Yosemite National Park, California.

Stratovolcanoes

The boundaries where tectonic plates push together are dotted with volcanoes. These are created as water and other material dragged beneath the crust changes the rock chemistry, making it melt. The molten rock erupts and builds up conical stratovolcanoes made of layers of lava and ash.

Explosive eruptions

The lava erupted from stratovolcanoes is thick and sticky, so it doesn't flow far. It can even solidify inside the crater, sealing it like a cork. Pressure then builds up within the volcano, until it is blown apart by a colossal explosion with the power of a nuclear bomb.

Ash plume rises high in the sky

Rivers of fire

Oceanic rifts and hotspot volcanoes such as those on Hawaii erupt very liquid lava. It flows over the landscape in rivers of fire, spreading out before solidifying to form very broad shield volcanoes. Some of these oceanic volcanoes are the biggest mountains on Earth.

Island arcs

Where plates are colliding beneath the ocean, the collision zones are marked by chains of volcanic islands such as the Aleutian Islands in the north Pacific, seen here from space. Each curved "island arc" traces the line of a plate boundary.

Minerals and rocks

All planets, including Earth, are made of elements – substances such as oxygen, hydrogen, silicon, and iron that contain just one type of atom. These combine to form various types of chemical compounds, including water and minerals such as the quartz that we use to make glass. Rocks are mixtures of different minerals. Some form as very hot molten rock cools and solidifies, while others are made from the fragments of other rocks.

Glittering crystals

Most minerals can form glittering geometric shapes called crystals. The shapes are defined by the way the atoms of the mineral bond together. These amethyst crystals are basically coloured quartz – a compound of silicon and oxygen that is a major component of rocks.

Igneous rock

When molten lava or underground magma cools and solidifies, its minerals form interlocking crystals, creating the very strong structure of an igneous rock such as granite. The crystals are often tiny, but as this granite was formed by very slow cooling, it has big crystals that are easy to see.

Mineral crystals are different colours

Erosion

As soon as rocks are exposed to the weather, they start breaking down. They are smashed into fragments like these, and eventually some minerals dissolve to form chemically altered materials such as clay. Water carries them off and deposits them in beds of soft sediment.

Sedimentary rock

Over millions of years soft sediments get harder as they are squeezed and cemented together by dissolved minerals. They form layers of sedimentary rock, such as these. Most are made of rock fragments, but some sedimentary rocks, such as limestones, are made of the skeletal remains of tiny living things.

Fossils

Soft sediments often contain the remains of dead animals. As the sediments harden, the animal remains are often preserved as fossils, like these ammonites – the shells of ancient sea creatures.

The rock cycle

If sedimentary rocks are buried and put under extreme pressure they can be squeezed, cooked, and changed into metamorphic rocks such as this very hard, layered gneiss. Eventually they may melt and erupt as lava from volcanoes, which then breaks down to form sedimentary rocks. This is called the rock cycle.

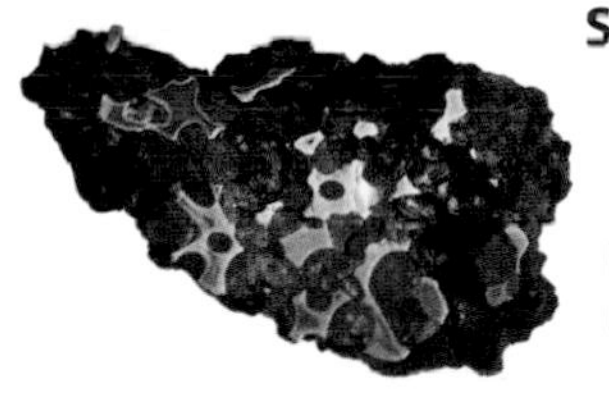

Space rock

Some rocks plunge to Earth from space in the shape of meteorites. Some are bits of shattered planets, like this fragment found in Antarctica. But other meteorites are made of the original raw material of the Solar System, including Earth itself.

Weather and climate

The world's weather is powered by the heat of the Sun. This warms oceans and continents, which heat the air and set it moving, generating wind. The Sun makes liquid water turn to airborne vapour that forms clouds, rain, and snow. But the average weather varies around the world, creating a wide variety of climates.

Clouds and rain

The Sun's heat turns water on land and in the sea into vapour, which rises into the air. This warm, moist air rises, expands, and cools, so the invisible water vapour turns into the tiny water droplets that form clouds. These grow until they fall as rain.

Pressure and wind

As warm air rises, it reduces the weight of air on the ground or sea below. This creates a zone of low atmospheric pressure, known as a cyclone. Surrounding air swirls into this to replace the rising air, creating wind.

Extreme weather

When rapidly rising warm air causes very low air pressure, air flows into the low-pressure zone faster, causing powerful winds that can reach hurricane force. The rising moist air also builds huge storm clouds with strong internal air currents that generate lightning, hail, and even tornadoes.

Climate zones

The Sun's rays strike the tropics head-on, but in the polar regions they are spread out and far less intense. The difference generates air currents in the atmosphere that create different climate zones such as tropical forests, subtropical deserts, and temperate grasslands.

The seasons

As Earth orbits the Sun, the tilt of the planet's spin axis places northern regions closer to the Sun in June, and further away in December. This causes summer and winter, and other seasonal changes such as monsoons.

Ireland has an oceanic climate

Cars produce a lot of carbon dioxide

Oceans and continents

Continents cool down in winter and warm up in summer, but ocean water changes temperature much more slowly. This gives many dry continental regions hot summers and very cold winters, while damper oceanic regions have cool summers and mild winters.

Climate change

Heat radiated from Earth is prevented from escaping by atmospheric gases such as carbon dioxide. We have added to these gases by burning fuels such as coal and oil, causing global warming.

Water and ice

Although water is a common substance in the Solar System, our planet seems to be the only place where it exists as a liquid, as a gas (water vapour), and as solid ice. This is what makes planet Earth so special, because if water were not able to change phase like this, there would be no weather, no rain, no life on land, and maybe no life at all.

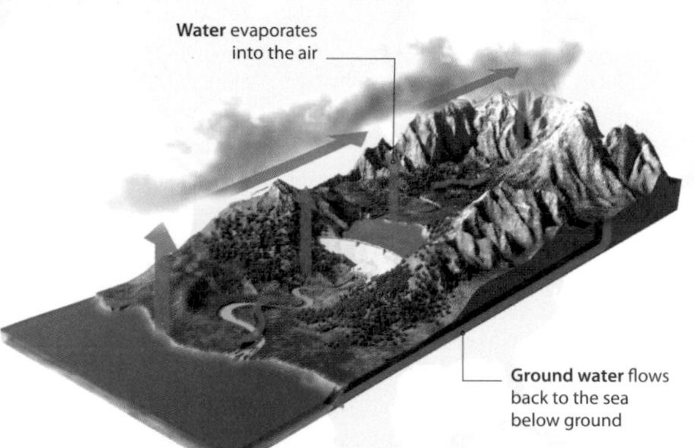

The water cycle

The heat of the Sun makes ocean water turn to water vapour and rise into the air. As it rises, it cools and forms clouds that may blow over land. The clouds spill rain (and snow), which drains off the land into rivers that flow back to the sea.

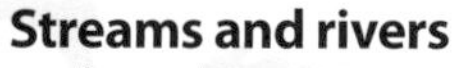

Streams and rivers

Water drains off the landscape in streams that trickle downhill and join up to form bigger rivers. In wet seasons these rivers may flood their valleys, creating broad, flat flood plains. Rivers wind slowly across these until they reach the salty ocean.

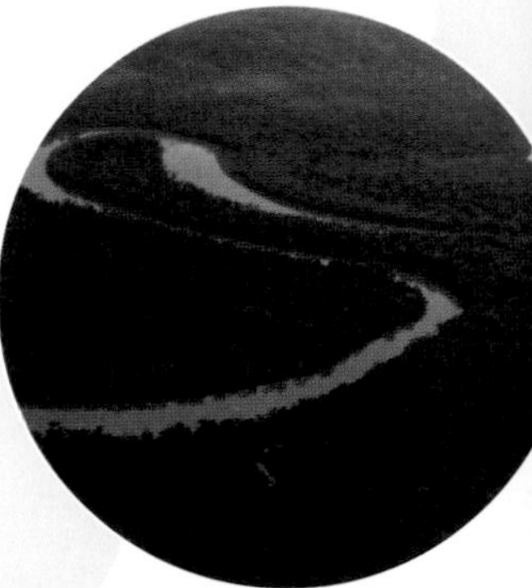

Underground water

A lot of rainwater seeps into the ground, where it is soaked up by porous rocks. But the water dissolves some rocks such as limestone, turning narrow fissures into spectacular cave systems that contain underground streams, rivers, and lakes.

Seas and salt lakes

Streams and rivers dissolve mineral salts and carry them to the sea. Over millions of years this has created the salty oceans. In hot climates the same process forms salt lakes, with fringes that sparkle with pale salt crystals.

Glaciers and ice sheets

In cold climates rain falls as snow. Any that does not melt in summer eventually turns to ice. This flows slowly downhill as glaciers that gouge broad valleys in mountain landscapes. In the polar regions it builds up into immensely thick ice sheets.

Icebergs

If the climate is cold enough, a glacier can flow right down to the sea, so its end – the ice front – floats on tidal water. The rising and falling tide makes great chunks of ice break off and float out to sea as icebergs.

Pack ice

Polar oceans freeze at the surface when air temperatures are low enough. The floating ice is thin at first, but thickens up into an almost continuous sheet of thick pack ice. In the Arctic, this is the home of the seal-hunting polar bear.

Life zones

Earth is unique in the Solar System because it supports complex forms of life. These form communities of plants, animals, fungi, and microbes that are known as ecosystems. The biggest of these are the major life zones of the planet, or biomes. They are defined by a combination of physical factors, such as geography and climate, and the nature of the living things that have evolved to suit each type of environment.

Deserts

Some regions are so dry that they can barely support life. The driest of these deserts are bare rock and sand, but others get just enough rain for specialized plants such as these cacti in Arizona. Most desert animals hide underground by day, and are active only at night.

Grasslands

Natural grasslands forms where the climate is too dry for forest, but not dry enough to create a desert. Some are tropical, like this African savanna, but there are also temperate steppes and prairies. The grass supports grazing herds and many smaller mammals, birds, and insects.

Forests

Trees usually need plenty of water, so forests grow in places that never really dry out. The rainforests of the warm tropics are the richest habitats on Earth, supporting most of the world's species. Most other forests, such as this one in France, grow in regions where cold winters limit the diversity of life.

Wetlands

Low-lying swamps and marshes are ideal places for life to flourish, especially in warm climates. In cooler regions, many wetlands evolve into acidic peat bogs built up from deep layers of moss, and supporting strange, insect-eating plants such as the Venus flytrap.

Polar regions

Continental ice sheets are polar deserts, but the tundra on their fringes defrosts in spring to allow a burst of colourful plant growth. This fuels a population explosion of insect life, attracting vast flocks of migrant birds that stay for the summer to breed before flying south again.

Oceans and seas

The oceans are the largest habitat on the planet, teeming with life from the icy polar seas to the coral reefs of the tropics. Most of it lives in the relatively warm, sunlit surface zone, but there is life even in the deepest, darkest, coldest water.

Answers

1 1a, 2a, 3c, 4b, 5b, 6c, 7c, 8c, 9d, 10a, 11a, 12d, 13d, 14d, 15b

2 1a, 2a, 3b, 4c, 5b, 6d, 7c, 8d, 9a, 10c, 11d, 12b, 13b, 14b, 15d, 16a, 17d, 18c, 19a, 20c

3 1a, 2a, 3c, 4b, 5c, 6c, 7b, 8d, 9b, 10c, 11a, 12b, 13c, 14a, 15a, 16d, 17b, 18d, 19d, 20d

4 1c, 2a, 3b, 4b, 5d, 6c, 7d, 8b, 9a, 10a, 11d, 12a, 13b, 14d, 15c

5 1b, 2b, 3a, 4a, 5b, 6d, 7c, 8a, 9a, 10a, 11c, 12c, 13c, 14d, 15b, 16b, 17d, 18d, 19c, 20d

6 1c, 2c, 3a, 4d, 5c, 6c, 7b, 8c, 9a, 10b, 11b, 12d, 13b, 14d, 15d, 16a, 17a, 18a, 19b, 20d

7 1d, 2b, 3c, 4c, 5a, 6a, 7c, 8b, 9b, 10d, 11d, 12c, 13a, 14b, 15d

8 1b, 2b, 3d, 4c, 5d, 6b, 7a, 8a, 9a, 10c, 11c, 12b, 13b, 14d, 15a, 16d, 17a, 18d, 19c, 20d

9 1d, 2b, 3c, 4d, 5b, 6d, 7a, 8b, 9b, 10a, 11a, 12c, 13b, 14a, 15c, 16a, 17c, 18d, 19c, 20d

10 1a, 2d, 3d, 4b, 5a, 6d, 7c, 8d, 9b, 10d, 11c, 12b, 13c, 14b, 15a

11 1a, 2b, 3a, 4d, 5a, 6b, 7b, 8d, 9d, 10d, 11c, 12c, 13c, 14c, 15d, 16b, 17b, 18a, 19a, 20c

12 1d, 2a, 3a, 4b, 5b, 6b, 7d, 8c, 9b, 10d, 11c, 12a, 13a, 14c, 15b, 16c, 17c, 18a, 19d, 20d

13 1c, 2d, 3c, 4a, 5b, 6d, 7d, 8b, 9c, 10c, 11a, 12b, 13d, 14a, 15a

14 1b, 2c, 3b, 4b, 5a, 6b, 7b, 8c, 9a, 10a, 11a, 12d, 13c, 14d, 15d, 16a, 17c, 18c, 19d, 20d

15 1c, 2d, 3a, 4a, 5d, 6d, 7c, 8c, 9b, 10a, 11c, 12b, 13a, 14b, 15d, 16c, 17b, 18a, 19b, 20d

16 1a, 2a, 3c, 4a, 5d, 6a, 7b, 8d, 9b, 10d, 11b, 12b, 13d, 14c, 15c

17 1d, 2b, 3b, 4c, 5b, 6a, 7d, 8c, 9c, 10b, 11c, 12a, 13b, 14d, 15a, 16d, 17c, 18a, 19c, 20a

18 1c, 2d, 3d, 4a, 5a, 6c, 7a, 8b, 9b, 10a, 11c, 12c, 13c, 14d, 15a, 16d, 17b, 18c, 19b, 20b

19 1d, 2b, 3d, 4a, 5b, 6b, 7d, 8d, 9a, 10a, 11c, 12a, 13b, 14c, 15c

20 1a, 2b, 3a, 4b, 5a, 6a, 7b, 8d, 9c, 10b, 11c, 12d, 13c, 14b, 15d, 16a, 17c, 18c, 19d, 20c

21 1c, 2d, 3b, 4b, 5c, 6b, 7a, 8d, 9d, 10c, 11a, 12d, 13d, 14d, 15c, 16c, 17b, 18a, 19a, 20a

22 1d, 2d, 3b, 4a, 5c, 6a, 7c, 8d, 9d, 10c, 11b, 12d, 13b, 14c, 15a

23 1b, 2b, 3a, 4c, 5d, 6b, 7a, 8d, 9d, 10a, 11a, 12b, 13c, 14d, 15c, 16b, 17c, 18d, 19c, 20a

24 1b, 2c, 3b, 4c, 5a, 6d, 7b, 8d, 9b, 10c, 11d, 12a, 13c, 14b, 15a, 16c, 17a, 18a, 19d, 20d

25 1a, 2c, 3d, 4c, 5b, 6d, 7d, 8b, 9d, 10c, 11a, 12a, 13a, 14d, 15c

26 1b, 2b, 3c, 4d, 5b, 6d, 7d, 8b, 9c, 10a, 11a, 12a, 13d, 14c, 15a, 16c, 17a, 18d, 19b, 20d

27 1d, 2a, 3b, 4c, 5a, 6d, 7d, 8c, 9c, 10a, 11c, 12a, 13a, 14c, 15b, 16d, 17b, 18c, 19b, 20b

28 1a, 2b, 3c, 4d, 5a, 6b, 7b, 8d, 9a, 10d, 11c, 12a, 13d, 14b, 15d

29 1b, 2b, 3a, 4a, 5a, 6b, 7a, 8c, 9d, 10d, 11d, 12d, 13b, 14d, 15a, 16b, 17c, 18c, 19c, 20c

30 1d, 2c, 3b, 4a, 5b, 6d, 7c, 8d, 9a, 10a, 11b, 12c, 13d, 14d, 15b, 16a, 17b, 18a, 19c, 20c

Answers

31 1b, 2a, 3b, 4b, 5a, 6c, 7d, 8c, 9d, 10a, 11c, 12b, 13d, 14c, 15c

32 1d, 2b, 3d, 4c, 5a, 6d, 7d, 8b, 9a, 10c, 11c, 12b, 13a, 14c, 15c, 16a, 17b, 18d, 19b, 20a

33 1d, 2c, 3a, 4b, 5c, 6a, 7d, 8b, 9b, 10b, 11c, 12d, 13d, 14c, 15b, 16a, 17c, 18d, 19a, 20a

34 1b, 2a, 3c, 4b, 5c, 6c, 7a, 8a, 9d, 10b, 11d, 12d, 13d, 14b, 15c

35 1d, 2a, 3a, 4a, 5c, 6b, 7b, 8b, 9d, 10a, 11d, 12d, 13c, 14c, 15d, 16b, 17b, 18c, 19c, 20a

36 1c, 2d, 3b, 4b, 5a, 6b, 7c, 8a, 9d, 10a, 11a, 12c, 13d, 14b, 15b, 16c, 17c, 18a, 19c, 20c

37 1a, 2c, 3b, 4d, 5a, 6c, 7c, 8d, 9b, 10d, 11b, 12d, 13c, 14a, 15a

38 1c, 2d, 3c, 4b, 5b, 6c, 7a, 8a, 9d, 10c, 11a, 12b, 13b, 14b, 15a, 16c, 17d, 18d, 19d, 20a

39 1a, 2a, 3a, 4c, 5d, 6d, 7c, 8b, 9d, 10c, 11a, 12b, 13b, 14b, 15c, 16d, 17c, 18b, 19a, 20d

40 1b, 2a, 3a, 4a, 5d, 6c, 7d, 8b, 9c, 10d, 11a, 12d, 13b, 14b, 15c

41 1c, 2a, 3a, 4b, 5d, 6b, 7d, 8c, 9a, 10d, 11c, 12a, 13a, 14b, 15b, 16d, 17c, 18d, 19c, 20b

42 1b, 2d, 3a, 4d, 5a, 6c, 7b, 8b, 9b, 10d, 11c, 12a, 13c, 14b, 15d, 16d, 17c, 18a, 19a, 20c

43 1c, 2b, 3c, 4c, 5d, 6b, 7a, 8c, 9a, 10b, 11a, 12a, 13d, 14b, 15d

44 1a, 2c, 3c, 4b, 5a, 6d, 7c, 8c, 9b, 10b, 11d, 12a, 13d, 14d, 15b, 16c, 17d, 18a, 19a, 20b

45 1c, 2b, 3b, 4b, 5c, 6a, 7c, 8c, 9d, 10b, 11a, 12a, 13d, 14b, 15a, 16d, 17a, 18c, 19d, 20d

46 1b, 2b, 3d, 4d, 5b, 6c, 7c, 8c, 9d, 10a, 11a, 12a, 13b, 14d, 15c

47 1a, 2a, 3b, 4c, 5a, 6a, 7c, 8b, 9c, 10d, 11c, 12d, 13b, 14b, 15a, 16c, 17d, 18d, 19b, 20d

48 1a, 2a, 3a, 4c, 5d, 6b, 7d, 8a, 9d, 10c, 11b, 12a, 13c, 14d, 15b, 16b, 17d, 18b, 19c, 20c

49 1b, 2c, 3c, 4b, 5d, 6a, 7a, 8d, 9c, 10d, 11d, 12c, 13d, 14a, 15a

50 1b, 2d, 3c, 4c, 5a, 6d, 7a, 8b, 9c, 10a, 11b, 12d, 13b, 14c, 15d, 16d, 17a, 18c, 19d, 20c

51 1b, 2b, 3b, 4c, 5b, 6a, 7b, 8a, 9a, 10d, 11a, 12d, 13a, 14d, 15c, 16c, 17d, 18c, 19d, 20d

52 1d, 2b, 3a, 4b, 5d, 6a, 7c, 8a, 9c, 10c, 11a, 12b, 13d, 14b, 15d

53 1a, 2b, 3b, 4c, 5c, 6d, 7d, 8b, 9c, 10a, 11d, 12c, 13d, 14b, 15a, 16a, 17d, 18b, 19d, 20a

54 1d, 2c, 3d, 4b, 5b, 6d, 7a, 8b, 9b, 10a, 11d, 12a, 13c, 14c, 15c, 16c, 17a, 18d, 19a, 20b

55 1c, 2d, 3a, 4d, 5a, 6d, 7c, 8d, 9b, 10a, 11d, 12c, 13b, 14c, 15a

56 1a, 2b, 3c, 4d, 5a, 6a, 7c, 8d, 9a, 10c, 11d, 12b, 13c, 14d, 15a, 16b, 17d, 18c, 19b, 20b

57 1a, 2a, 3d, 4d, 5b, 6b, 7b, 8c, 9c, 10c, 11c, 12c, 13d, 14b, 15d, 16c, 17b, 18a, 19a, 20a

58 1c, 2a, 3d, 4c, 5c, 6b, 7d, 8d, 9b, 10b, 11c, 12d, 13a, 14b, 15a

59 1d, 2b, 3d, 4a, 5c, 6a, 7d, 8c, 9a, 10a, 11b, 12b, 13a, 14c, 15d, 16c, 17b, 18b, 19c, 20d

60 1d, 2d, 3c, 4a, 5c, 6b, 7c, 8b, 9a, 10c, 11b, 12a, 13b, 14a, 15a, 16a, 17d, 18c, 19b, 20d

Acknowledgments

DK would like to thank: Jenny Sich for proofreading; Sreshtha Bhattacharya, Vibha Malhotra, James Mitchem, Archana Ramachandran, and Garima Sharma for additional editorial work; and Arup Giri, Rakesh Khundongbam, Vaibhav Rastogi, Anis Sayyed, Anuj Sharma, and Aanchal Singal for additional design work.

The publisher would like to thank the following for their kind permission to reproduce their photographs:
(Key: a – above; b – below/bottom; c – centre; f – far; l – left; r – right; t – top)

6–7 Dorling Kindersley: Jamie Marshall. **10 Dorling Kindersley:** Jon Hughes / Bedrock Studios (tl). **12–13 Corbis:** Dave Reede / AgStock Images. **18 U.S. Geological Survey:** Austin Post (tl). **20 Dorling Kindersley:** Katy Williamson (bc). **23 NASA:** Jacques Descloitres, MODIS Rapid Response Team / GSFC (tr). **25 Dreamstime.com:** Stanko Mravljak (clb). **31 Dorling Kindersley:** Natural History Museum, London (tl). **36 Dorling Kindersley:** Jamie Marshall (c). **37 Corbis:** Image Plan (t). **38 Dorling Kindersley:** Natural History Museum, London (tl). **43 PunchStock:** Photodisc (tr). **48–49 Dorling Kindersley:** Thomas Marent. **49 NASA:** Reto Stöckli, Nazmi El Saleous, and Marit Jentoft-Nilsen (cr). **53 Dorling Kindersley:** Natural History Museum, London (tr). **60 Dorling Kindersley:** Dan Bannister (br). **66 Dreamstime.com:** Designpicssub (bc). **72 Dorling Kindersley:** Lindsey Stock (tr). **80 Dorling Kindersley:** Barrie Watts (cr). **92 Alamy Images:** Chad Ehlers (cl). **96–97 Dorling Kindersley:** NASA / digitaleye / Jamie Marshall. **102–103 Alamy Images:** Martin Strmiska. **106 Dorling Kindersley:** Nasa / Digitaleye / Jamie Marshall (tr). **111 Dorling Kindersley:** Judith Miller / Wallis and Wallis (tr). **116 Corbis:** Oliver Berg / dpa (tr). **123 PunchStock:** Digital Vision (cr). **124 Dorling Kindersley:** Katy Williamson (bl). **126–127 Dorling Kindersley:** NASA (c). **NASA:** International Astronomical Union (b). **126 Science Photo Library:** Henning Dalhoff (tr). **127 NASA:** Johnson Space Center (cl); (br). **128 Getty Images:** Planet Observer (b). **129 NASA:** (cr). **130 Corbis:** Roger Ressmeyer (tr). **U.S. Geological Survey:** D. Ravat (br). **131 Corbis:** Akhtar Soomro / epa (b). **133 Corbis:** NASA (br); Image Plan (tl). **Dreamstime.com:** Wdeon (cr). **Getty Images:** Robert Reiff (bl). **134 Dorling Kindersley:** Jorn Bohmer-Olsen / Rolf Sørensen (bl). **135 Dorling Kindersley:** Natural History Museum, London (bl). **136 PunchStock:** Photodisc (bl). **139 Getty Images:** Kevin Schafer (b). **141 Alamy Images:** Alaska Stock (cr). **NOAA:** Papahānaumokuākea Marine National Monument (bl)

Jacket images: Front: **Getty Images:** GK Hart / Vikki Hart